To Jenny

from Graham

December 2019

AT THE SHARP END!

AT THE SHARP END!

By

GEORGE H. PARKER

GLASGOW
BROWN, SON & FERGUSON, LTD., NAUTICAL PUBLISHERS
4-10 DARNLEY STREET

First Edition – – 1992

ISBN 0 85174 610 1

© 1992 BROWN, SON & FERGUSON, LTD., GLASGOW, G41 2SD
Made and Printed in Great Britain

PREFACE

THIS book is concerned with the 'rough and tumble' of the Shipbuilding Industry, and in particular, my involvement in its management.

Apart from a few chapters, one devoted to my grandfather's and father's contribution to the Industry, the contents trace my own career from apprenticeship and initial training, through the management of a single ship to the management of a shipyard's production and ultimately to executive control of a number of shipyards.

My younger son, despite my misgivings, is carrying on the family tradition. I thought it appropriate to record, for his benefit, this true shipbuilding story. This book is accordingly dedicated to him.

I hope that in the following pages, something of the struggles, joys and sorrows of building ships may become evident. This great Industry became almost a way of life to our family. I certainly believe that few other industries can offer more excitement, drama and satisfaction in equal measure.

Just as U.K. built steam railway engines and motorcycles have passed into folklore, but retain fond memories and an abiding interest for many who were neither associated with their manufacture nor with their operation, so it may be with U.K. Shipbuilding.

I make no claim to be one of the foremost shipbuilders of my time. However, I can claim to have a lifetime of experience in this great Industry. Unlike many of my contemporaries, this experience included the building of passenger liners. In the general public's mind at least, these represent perhaps the most glamorous type of ship.

What follows therefore is our family's experience of building a variety of ships in many of the shipbuilding centres of the United Kingdom.

ACKNOWLEDGEMENTS

MY grateful thanks are due to my wife without whose encouragement this book would never have been written.

Encouragement apart, she also undertook the typing of the manuscript and numerous reviews of its contents while at the same time offering constructive suggestions for improvements. For this I am grateful.

My thanks are also due to my son-in-law who undertook to convert the manuscript into bookform and thereby rendered it more acceptable I believe to potential publishers.

Finally, my thanks are due to the following for permission to reproduce the photographs:—

Norman Brown & Company, Dundee.
Norman Burniston Photography, Greenock.
Ralston Photographers, Glasgow.
John Brown, Clydebank.
The Scottish Office, Edinburgh.
FotoFlite, New Romney.
Turners Photography, Thornaby.
British Shipbuilders, Newcastle upon Tyne.
Swan Hunter International, Newcastle upon Tyne.
Aeromarine Photographic Ltd., Manston.
J. D. Forbes, Dundee.

CONTENTS

Chapter 1. — EARLY DAYS.
         2. — TWO GENERATIONS OF SHIPBUILDING.
         3. — "FUN AND GAMES" WITH THE LABOUR FORCE.
         4. — SHIPBUILDING PRIOR TO 1950.
         5. — APPRENTICESHIP.
         6. — SERVICE INTERLUDE.
         7. — LITHGOWS LTD.
         8. — THE CLYDE SHIPBUILDERS ASSOCIATION.
         9. — JOHN BROWN & CO. (CLYDEBANK) LTD.
       10. — THE LAUNCH OF THE *QE2*.
       11. — MERGER DISCUSSIONS.
       12. — UPPER CLYDE SHIPBUILDERS.
       13. — SWAN HUNTER SHIPBUILDERS LTD.
       14. — *VISTAFJORD*.
       15. — SMITHS DOCK CO. LTD.
       16. — SMITHS DOCK CO. LTD. POST-NATIONAL-ISATION.
       17. — SHIPREPAIR DIVISION.
       18. — AUSTIN & PICKERSGILL LIMITED.
       19. — NORTH EAST SHIPBUILDERS LIMITED.
       20. — A FEW SHIPBUILDERS.
       21. — TWO "TRUE BLUE" SHIPOWNERS.
       22. — "BITS & PIECES".
       23. — POSTSCRIPT.

LIST OF ILLUSTRATIONS

PAGE

A small launch party at Dunlop Bremner's yard 1921
(my grandfather is third from left). 8

Cargo/passenger motor vessel *Charon*, 1936. 13

SS *Empire Bard* — my mother's "ugly duckling" 1942. 14

Auxiliary aircraft carrier HMS *Activity*, 1942. 16

MV *Diomed*, 1956. 18

My father's first launch as managing director, April 1949. 19

MV *Kaldfonn* on trials, September 1955. 45

The pilgrim/cargo vessel SS *Saudi*, April 1956. 49

Jack-up drilling rig *Orion* completed 30th June 1966. 63

My first speaking engagement! Acceptance of drilling rig
Orion, 21st June 1966 (my wife in the centre). 64

Launch of the assault ship HMS *Intrepid*, 25th June 1964. ... 65

TSMV *Kingsholm*, completed 11th March 1966. 68

Lecturing Manny Shinwell during visit to *QE2* by Harold
Wilson and a large deputation of MPs, summer 1967. 73

Inspecting the launch arrangements of *QE2* in the company of
Her Majesty the Queen, 20th September 1967. 77

I was mightily relieved! 79

A striking photograph of a British India Steam Navigation
Company cargo liner ready for launch at Swan Hunter's
Neptune Yard. 90

One of the Swan Hunter super tankers leaving the river Tyne
for trials, November 1971. 92

Successful sea trials off the Northumberland coast TSMV
Vistafjord, February 1973. 99

Blue Star Lines MV *Afric Star* at sea during sea trials,
(sister ship of MV *Almeria Star*). 106

PAGE

"Cutting the christening cake". Commissioning of MV
Manchester Vanguard at Southbank, 1977. 108

MV *Manchester Vanguard* ready for commissioning and
handover at Southbank, 13th October 1977. 109

Shiprepairing at Tyne Shiprepair Ltd., May 1981. 129

I accept on behalf of the builders, a pair of Ethiopian
elephant tusks, 14th May 1984. 152

My wife in conversation with Gordon Bagier, MP at the
reception following the launch of the first of two cargo
vessels for the Ethiopian National Shipping Line,
14th May 1984. 153

"Lets both push the boat out". Launch of the second
Ethiopian cargo vessel, 24th October 1984. 155

Christening the Yugoslav way! MV *Pomorac*, 30th September
1985. 162

Signing the Danish ferry contract at Knightsbridge, 18th July
1986. 170

To Alan

THOUGHTS ON LEADERSHIP

Leadership is the courage to admit mistakes,
The vision to welcome change,
The enthusiasm to motivate others,
And the confidence to stay out of step when
everyone else is marching to the wrong tune.

E. M. Estes
President
General Motors Corporation

CHAPTER 1

EARLY DAYS

I was born in a house overlooking the River Tay in the East end of Dundee on 10th December, 1928. From my bedroom window I was able to see the shipyard with its six slipways stretched along the riverbank. The river at this point is some 2 miles wide and across from the shipyard rise the rolling green hills of Fife.

Dundee was then Scotland's third city and referred to as the City of the three "J's" — Jute, Jam and Journalism. This was not strictly true, since both the Jute and Jam Industries were in decline. Within a few years, the Caledon Shipbuilding and Engineering Co. Ltd., would become Dundee's largest employer.

Journalism played a part in many young boys' lives then, as now, for Dundee was the home of the "Dandy" and "Beano" comics. In fact, the father of one of my early classmates wrote the "Desperate Dan" strip in the "Dandy" — Cow pie, Shark & Chips and all that! He may have been a "touch" eccentric, just like another Dundee worthy — McGonagall, the poet!

McGonagall wrote doggeral and his friends encouraged him to write more and more of his so-called verse, on a variety of subjects. His output was heroic! A few lines will illustrate his undoubted talent!

O, beautiful City of Glasgow, which stands on the River Clyde,
How happy should the people be which in ye reside,
Because it is the most enterprising city of the present day,
Whatever anybody else may say,

The ships which lie at the Broomielaw are most beautiful to see,
They are bigger and better than any in Dundee.

*   *   *   *   *

At a farewell lunch before McGonagall left Dundee for London,
a quarter stone of sausages was offered for the best poem "on"
McGonagall. One of the stanzas runs:—
"Ower a' the bards together put,
Frae Friockheim to Japan,
He towers aloft, beyond dispute,
Creation's greatest man".
In the early 30s, my father was the shipyard manager and talk at
home was frequently of ships and shipbuilding. From the age of five
or so, I never wanted to do anything other than build ships. Most
Sunday mornings my father would walk my brother and me
through the yard — platers sheds, building berths and sometimes
on to ships fitting-out afloat. The place was deserted, with the sole
exception of a maintenance engineer inside the compressor house
and of course the gateman. Sunday overtime was practically
unheard of at that time.

I began to learn how ships were constructed and began my
life-long love affair with the shape of ships — the round of bilge, the
sheer of the decks, the flare of the bow and the run of the stern lines.

My love of ships was further enhanced by frequent visits to Port
Glasgow on the Lower Clyde, the home of my grandparents. My
grandmother's ground floor flat was sited on the top of Clune Brae
and the view from the lounge windows was indeed spectacular. Far
below, forming almost a continuous line, lay five shipyards along
the riverbank. A few miles to the East, Dumbarton rock was clearly
visible, while the Clyde widens out at Port Glasgow to form the
Tail-of-the-Bank. Thereafter at Gourock, the river swings South
and is lost to sight. Across the river lies Helensburgh and the
entrance to the Gareloch, with Loch Long and the Holy Loch
beyond. This magnificent view is capped by the mountains in the
background.

My fascination as a young boy was not with the view but with the
ships. At low tide, even the smallest vessels could not traverse the
channel between the exposed sandbanks. Activity then was centred
at the Tail-of-the-Bank, where ships were gathering, awaiting the

tide. When the sandbanks disappeared and with sufficient water available, a never-ending stream of ships passed below these windows, both outward and homeward bound.

In those days, Glasgow was a major port and boasted a number of indigenous shipowners. It served them, as well as other U.K. and foreign owners. Ships of every type imaginable came into view. Anchor Line passenger ships from Karachi and Bombay; Donaldson Lines cargo/passenger ships from Montreal; City Line and Clan Line vessels from Africa and India; Paddy Henderson Lines cargo and passenger ships from Rangoon; Blue Funnel Line ships from the Far East; Hogarth and Denholm Line Tramp Steamers and a host of other cargo vessels. Smart passenger vessels, owned by Burns Laird Line sailed past, maintaining their frequent service to Belfast, while the small ships of the Clyde Shipping Co. were doing the same for Southern Ireland. Small oil tankers made their way to the oil terminal at Bowling, while hopper barges, tugs, "puffers" and Clyde passenger steamers were continuously in evidence. Canadian Pacific Liners did not steam up river, but anchored at the Tail-of-the-Bank and there disembarked their passengers. Their elegant white profiles could readily be made out through binoculars. Occasionally, Cunarders also arrived from Canada.

My other grandparents also lived in Port Glasgow, but their house did not afford a view of the river. This oversight was compensated by the conversation, which was frequently about ships and shipbuilding!

Until the age of ten, I attended Dundee High School, but in 1940, the fear of an invasion from across the North Sea prompted my parents to despatch my brother and me to Morrison's Academy in Crieff as boarders. During the holidays, I was sometimes invited to the launch of a ship and savoured the exciting moments as the last blocks and shores were removed from the bottom of the ship by the shipwrights. All then was silent as the sponsor named the vessel, smashed the bottle against the bow and immediately thereafter the ship began to move smoothly down the ways, gaining speed all the time, until she was fully afloat. It was not until many years afterwards that I was to learn of things than can and do go wrong at launches. But at the age of twelve, it seemed perfection.

Soon after the outbreak of War, merchant ships already under construction, together with those not yet started to build, were requisitioned by the Admiralty. No longer were they recognisable as company ships, for they all sailed out from the Tay in drab grey paint, guns mounted fore and aft and loaded with strange-looking gear which hung over the bow.

Dundee became a submarine base and units of the British, French, Dutch, Norwegian and Polish Navies, were located there. Early in the war, Polish soldiers were billeted for a time in Stirling Castle, some 40 miles away. Frequently at weekends, Polish officers in uniform would stroll around Dundee City Centre. Dundonians called them the B.E.F. — Back Every Friday!

The submarine flotillas were of course engaging the enemy in the North Sea, off the Norwegian Coast and elsewhere and did not escape losses and damage. This gave rise to a huge increase in workload for the shipyard. Arriving home for the Christmas Holidays, I found our house full of naval officers. Admiralty inspectors and superintendents were frequent visitors to the house all the year round.

To digress for a moment. After the War my mother was interviewing a local lady for the job of "home help". Deciding to employ her, she enquired of her name. The lady replied, — "Och, I'm married to one of thae Poles, but just call me Winnie!"

On my numerous visits to the shipyard during holidays from school, I met a number of shipyard personnel. Of these, the most memorable were Head Foremen — the "sergeant-majors" of the production facility. Two of these worthies I recall with affection. The first, Donald Cameron, was Head Foreman Painter and came originally from Port Glasgow on the Lower Clyde, where my father had grown up. He was a cheerful man, with a round red face, topped of course, by a bowler hat spotted with red lead. His nose was tinged with blue and as my father put it — "due no doubt to the cold East wind that prevails in these parts!"

Going up the gangway onto a ship afloat and nearing completion, all seemed noise, bodies and chaos. Donald, whose gloss paint coatings were supposed to be applied after all other work had been completed, frequently found his beautiful paintwork ruined by some other trade whose work was incomplete. My father would enquire as to progress. Donald would smile a rueful smile and say — "My work is shining out like a shilling on a sweep's a - - - ".

The other worthy I recall with pleasure was Alan Thomson — Head Foreman Riveter. He was known everywhere as, "Po" Thomson — since apparently as a small boy in his home town of Clydebank, he for some reason stuck a chamber pot on his head, but found he couldn't remove it.

Alan was a big heavy man, with a lined weather-beaten face and of course bowler-hatted at work. As a young man, employed as a riveter in John Brown's Yard, he had won a Nationwide competition for driving the most rivets in a single working day, as part of the War effort.

He "emigrated" to Dundee and became a shop steward and quickly became the bane of management's existence. It occurred to the management of the time that Alan might work in their favour if they made him a foreman. It worked like a charm and ultimately as Head Foreman, he was the scourge of riveters everywhere.

The transformation in "Po's" appearance from work to leisure had to be seen to be believed. At weekends, he was immaculate in a well-cut, three-piece checked suit, bow tie, brown brogues and a checked cap festooned with salmon flies and accompanied by his beautiful black labrador.

He was an expert game fisherman, as well as being a crack shot. The plain fact was however, he poached. After the War and during the season, very rarely would a Saturday evening pass without Alan calling at the house to hand in either a whole salmon or a brace of grouse or pheasant. But he was such a card and was so expert at these activities, that he gradually came to be invited to "official shoots" with the local gentry. This way, the gentry could be assured of a good "bag". Most weekends in the shooting season, Alan was on official business on one estate or another.

One weekend however, no invitation arrived. So he went salmon fishing instead — unofficially. As he made his way back to his car, with his trusty dog and loaded with tackle and his catch, he failed to notice a bull in the field he was traversing. The bull charged and gored Alan. Before he could reach the fence, now in acute pain, the bull gored him a second time. The third charge put him clean over the fence.

He was off work for six months. Both legs were black from ankle to groin and there were other internal injuries. When finally he did return to work, there were two huge greetings for him from "his" riveters, daubed in white paint on the side of the platers shed. The first read — "Have a go Po said the bull" and the other read — "The first toss that Tamson ever lost".

During the close season Alan made trout and salmon flies using the hackles of the game birds he had previously shot. It remains a mystery to me how these huge hands (they could hold seven tennis balls), could so delicately dress a fly to perfection. So good were they that he sold them to one of Scotland's foremost tackle shops.

Some years later I received a greetings telegram from Alan, on the occasion of my marriage, which read — "Let the grouse season never start and the deer season never end".

The war came to an end and in the year following, so did my schooling. I had long since decided to try to make a career of shipbuilding. My parents and grandparents encouraged me.

CHAPTER 2

TWO GENERATIONS OF SHIPBUILDING

I had seen at first hand how much my father enjoyed his work. I also had the same impression from my grandfather who completed no less than sixty-two and a half years in the shipbuilding industry. Born at Tyneside, he started his apprenticeship as a ship draughtsman in Dobson's yard following which he moved to Swan Hunter and Wigham Richardson Limited. He then joined Harland & Wolff's Drawing Office in Belfast. He later returned to the North East where he worked in the Drawing Office of Sir Railton Dixon at Stockton-on-Tees. Gaining experience and a little promotion with each move, he than transferred to a small shipyard in Londonderry for a second spell in Ulster, before finally moving to the Lower Clyde as Chief Draughtsman with the Clyde Shipbuilding and Engineering Company Limited.

Shortly afterwards, he was invited to join a group of engineers and businessmen interested in re-opening the old shipyard of David J. Dunlop in Port Glasgow. He duly became Shipbuilding Director of the newly-styled Dunlop Bremner & Co. Limited, which re-opened in 1911. The business prospered and the advent of war in 1914 brought much new work.

After 1919, the order book remained high because of the need to replace wartime losses. (*See illustration*). But by 1921/2 the business was very slack. The severe work shortage was being felt across the whole U.K. shipbuilding industry. It has to be remembered that around this time, the U.K. shipbuilding industry accounted for 60% of all newbuilding in the World.

A small launch party at Dunlop Bremner's yard 1921 (my grandfather is third from left).

A new company was set up, with the name of National Shipbuilders Securities Limited, partly financed by the shipbuilders themselves, with the object of buying out some existing shipyards and thereafter closing them, in order to reduce capacity. One of the many companies to accept the offer of closure was Dunlop Bremner's. The terms were quite generous, which no doubt they had to be.

The Chairman of National Shipbuilders Securities Limited was Sir James Lithgow, whose two shipyards in Port Glasgow were next door to Dunlop Bremner. Sir James offered my grandfather a position as Lithgow's permanent representative on the Shipbuilding Employers Federation (the body that dealt with labour relations at national level). This he accepted and remained in for no less than 25 years, retiring at the age of 77 somewhat reluctantly because of increasing blindness.

My father commenced his apprenticeship as a ships draughtsman with Ferguson Brothers of Port Glasgow in 1915. The other half of the semi-detached house in which the family lived was occupied by some of the Fergusons. His friend Louis, of exactly the same age, had decided like my father to pursue a shipbuilding career. It was arranged that Louis Ferguson would start in Dunlop Bremner's Drawing Office, while on the same day Cameron Parker would start in Ferguson's Drawing Office. Halfway through their apprenticeship they were both called up with the Royal Scots and sent to Mullingar in Southern Ireland. At the end of hostilities they returned together to resume their apprenticeships. On the day their apprenticeships were completed, Louis received an increase in wages, due to his new status as a journeyman draughtsman. Cameron Parker was sacked. The reason given was simple — shortage of work.

He remained out of work for some six months, but ultimately successfully applied to join William Beardmore & Co. Limited at Dalmuir (next to Clydebank) as a journeyman draughtsman. This was a big yard, full of work at the time, including battleships and Italian passenger liners. A year or so later in 1922, he was working on steelwork plans of a new Battle-cruiser for the Royal Navy — the improved *Hood* class, when the Chief Draughtsman advised him that this work was now to be abandoned and since there were no orders and little prospect of obtaining any, it was with the utmost regret . . .

Six months later, he moved to Vickers-Armstrong Limited at Barrow-in-Furness, again as a steelwork draughtsman. This large yard had been successful in landing an order from the Orient Line for 4-20,000 ton gross passengers liners. The yard had also acquired a new General Manager and Shipyard Manager, both from Clydeside. Their first move was to fire most of the Drawing Office staff and recruit replacements from Clydeside. Hence the need for draughtsmen. When in due course, my mother arrived in Barrow to set up her first home, women strangers used to spit at her in the street. Such was the understandable hatred by the local families who had lost their jobs for the incomers who had gained them.

Some managers in those days could be very harsh. Everyone lived in perpetual fear of losing his job. Most days one or more workmen were fired on the flimsiest pretext. Even the Chief Draughtsman, (Lord of 150 ships draughtsman), lived in dread of losing his job. He wore his hat at all times in the office. It was believed that this was in order to leave the office quicker when he finally received his marching orders.

On one occasion one of the production bosses strode into the Drawing Office in a raging temper. His target was a draughtsman whose plan was impatiently awaited in the shipyard. Before he could reach the offending person, he fell headlong over a stool and for a moment lay prostrate on the floor. Total silence reigned. He stood up, said nothing and walked out of the office. Within half an hour, a typed notice appeared on the Notice Board, banning all drawing office stools and a squad of labourers arrived to remove the offending stools and burn them.

In 1924, the *Orama*, first of the four Orient Liners, was launched. One of the Assistant Managers became ill and a replacement was needed. My father of course knew nothing of this, but was sent for by the General Manager. He was offered the job and smilingly accepted. The General Manager snarled — "Don't get any fancy ideas above your station. You're not an Assistant Manager, you're an outside bloody draughtsman. If you're still there when the ship is finished, you'll return to the Drawing Office when you will then forfeit the five shillings per week increase you will get while outside.".

He lasted until the ship was delivered and was duly returned to the Drawing Office losing five shillings per week in the process. On a subsequent occasion, he was ordered "outside" again, accompanied by a five shillings per week increase. Again he lost the increase when he was returned to the office on completion of the ship. On the strength of a third stint "outside", he got married. Some time later, "they" lost five shillings per week. In 1928 my father successfully applied for the job of Assistant Shipyard Manager at the Caledon Yard in Dundee.

The Caledon Shipbuilding & Engineering Co. Limited was a medium-sized shipyard with six berths, capable at that time of constructing ships up to 500 feet in length. The company had its own Engine Works and Boiler Shop located half a mile from the shipyard. A modest amount of shiprepairing was undertaken, utilizing a small dry dock owned by Dundee Harbour Trust. The company chairman, P. S. Brown, had been at the helm since the founding of the business in 1896. He was a director of Brown & Tawse Limited, steel stockists, also of Dundee.

In 1928, shipbuilding activity was pretty slack and so my father spent a good deal of time touting for repair work. This entailed boarding ships as they arrived at the port and asking the captain (or the Superintendent, if available) whether any repair work was needed. When repairs were required, the price for each single repair had to be given "on the spot". If the price was acceptable, then the deadline for completion was agreed and work could begin. This first involved going round the homes of the men who would undertake the work, since they were not continuously employed. They all jumped at the chance of reporting the next morning for some few days of work.

Shortly after arriving in Dundee, my father, along with other members of the staff, were placed on "half pay", due to the shortage of new work. Grass began to grow on the berths. In 1932 the Managing Director retired and his place was taken by the Shipyard Manager. Much I believe to my father's surprise, he was appointed Shipyard Manager.

The shipbuilding slump continued and only two vessels were delivered in 1933. One of these was quite notable — the *Gorgon*, a passenger/cargo motorship for Alfred Holt & Co. Ltd. of Liverpool (The Blue Funnel Line).

Between 1934 and 1935 only five further vessels were delivered, all of small size. But 1935 saw some improvement in the market and a number of orders were taken.

In 1936, no fewer than twelve ships were delivered. Admittedly five of these were coasters, one a harbour tug and one a wine carrier. But the remaining vessels were all sizeable and included a 9,000 tons deadweight tramp steamer, three 6,000 tons deadweight cargo vessels and the *Charon*, (*See illustration*), a larger version of the passenger/cargo motorship built for Alfred Holt & Co. three years earlier.

The shipping market continued to improve and the yard was kept busy for the three years up to the outbreak of World War II. In 1938 one notable ship was delivered — the twin-screw motor vessel *Glenearn*, built for the Glen Line Ltd. of London (a subsidiary of Alfred Holt). This ship was the first of three built at the yard. The later pair, *Glengyle* and *Glenartney* were taken over by the Admiralty before delivery in 1940. These three ships, together with their two sister ships built by Scotts of Greenock, took part in many War exploits, principally because of their speed. At 19 knots they were fast indeed for their time.

In 1938 my father was appointed a Director of the company and was now up to his neck in building ships.

The company had long-established connections with a number of U.K. shipowners, including Alfred Holt & Co. Ltd. (who owned 41% of the company equity), Watts, Watts & Co. Ltd. of London, Colonial Sugar Refining Co. Ltd,. Raeburn & Verel of Glasgow and the General Steam Navigation Co. of London. In addition they had more recently established connections with a number of Australian shipowners, including Adelaide Steamship Co. Ltd., McIlwraith McEacharn Ltd. and Huddart Parker Ltd.

The War years proved very demanding for the shipbuilding industry. At the beginning, ships building or on order were requisitioned by the Admiralty, but soon afterwards many yards, including Caledon, began turning out standard ships designed to maximise production, in order to quickly replace ships sunk by U-boats. One of these was the *Empire Bard*, which my mother launched. Unfortunately the ship was extremely ugly, but at least she had a fine sponsor. (*See illustration*).

The Controller of Merchant Shipbuilding for the whole of the U.K. including Northern Ireland, was Sir James Lithgow. A shipbuilder of international repute, he was up to the outbreak of hostilities, probably Scotland's foremost industrialist. He was a restless man with boundless energy and drive — just the man for the

Cargo/passenger motor vessel *Charon*, 1936.

SS *Empire Bard* — my mother's "ugly duckling" 1942.

job. He constantly toured the country, exhorting bigger efforts from shipbuilders. Every second Sunday, he would be driven from his home near Port Glasgow to Croftinloan School near Comrie in Perthshire, where his son Bill would be uplifted and then on to Dundee for a whirlwind tour of the yard. On one such occasion, he insisted that the yard squeeze yet another ship into its already tight programme and deliver it before the year-end. The shipyard at this time was "flat out" with a ship on all six berths, several outfitting afloat and with damage repairs being undertaken to submarines, destroyers and merchant ships. The standard ship in question was the *Empire Heywood*, whose keel was laid towards the end of June, 1941 and was delivered on the 31st of December. The progress photographs record the absolutely astounding speed of construction!

During the War years, the yard also built Admiralty fleet oilers, together with corvettes and frigates. Perhaps the most unusual ship built during this period was one of the Alfred Holt ships requisitioned by the Admiralty. Halfway through construction, the ship was converted into an auxiliary aircraft carrier — H.M.S. *Activity*. (*See illustration*).

The War came to an end and with it came the need to replace Wartime losses. Owners clamoured to place orders and the yard remained extremely busy. The next ten years or so, were the most profitable in the company's history. The first two ships to appear resplendent in their company colours after the War were the *Stentor* and *Rhexenor*, both for Alfred Holt. The same company then began to place orders for a large number of their newly-designed "Anchises" class of cargo liner. These superb ships were built by a selected few U.K. shipyards including Vickers Naval Yard on Tyneside, Harland & Wolff of Belfast and Scotts of Greenock. The ships were handsome and very stoutly built. Their scantlings were way in excess of that laid down by the Classification Society. Their owners insured their own vessels, which was one good reason for the additional strength built into their ships. They also plied slightly different routes to other vessels making a passage to the same port. This ensured that should any mishap occur to one of their fleet, the first vessel to arrive on the scene would be another one of their fleet. The "Anchises" class were of around 8,000 tons gross and were powered by a Burmeister & Wain Diesel Engine to give a speed of

Auxiliary aircraft carrier HMS *Activity*, 1942.

16½ knots. The accommodation was arranged amidships and included facilities for twelve passengers. The long centre-castle was surmounted by the world-renowned large blue and black funnel.

Including the first of class "Anchises", Caledon built no fewer than thirteen ships of this type, including derivitives, up to 1960. One of these, the *Diomed* was the cadet ship of the fleet and not long before its completion in 1956, my father learned that my brother, Cameron, was to be appointed its 4th Engineer. (*See illustration*). The inspection of the 4th Engineer's cabin thereafter became of compelling interest to him in his daily rounds of the yard!

In April 1949, returning by sleeper train to Dundee, following the Royal Institution of Naval Architects Dinner in London the previous evening, my father was awoken early by the coach attendant. He was informed that the Managing Director in the next door berth had died sometime during the night. Some little time later my father succeeded as Managing Director. (*See illustration*).

From this point more and more new customers placed orders with Caledon. Among these were, Bowater Steamships (3 ships), Ellerman Lines Ltd. (6 ships) and numerous others who placed a single order. The old customers continued to place business with the company, like Watts, Watts, & Co. Ltd. (5 ships) and many others.

One of the notable features of Caledon's output during the post war period was the sheer variety of ships built. For example, two ships were built for the Straits Steamship Co. Ltd. of Singapore. These little twin-screw vessels were designed to operate in shallow rivers deep in the jungle and were able to carry 40 passengers as well as general cargo. Two vehicular ferries were built for Dundee Harbour Trust, as well as smart little coasters for the Clyde Shipping Co.'s Irish Trade. Three oil tankers were constructed, one for Swedish owners and two for Iver Bugge of Larvik in Norway. The second of these, the *Storaas* delivered in 1954, was at 16,500 tons deadweight, the largest ship built in the east of Scotland. Despite this great range of products, the company was however recognised as one of the foremost builders of high-class cargo liners.

In 1963, Edgar P. Brown, Caledon's Chairman since 1946, retired at the age of 75. His cousin, who had been a director of the

MV *Diomed*, 1956.

My father's first launch as managing director, April 1949.

company for many years and had been expected to succeed him, declined to assume the office. My father was asked to become Chairman, combining this with his duties as Managing Director. He accepted with considerable reluctance, because he did not consider that he could bring to the office sufficient experience in financial matters. Although never interfering in shipbuilding affairs, Edgar Brown had been a tower of strength combining a breadth of vision with financial astuteness. The other problem that concerned my father was his health and in particular his heart.

The trouble began in 1952, when he was Vice-President of the Shipbuilding Employers Federation (S.E.F.). As an office-bearer he was required to be in attendance at all meetings, normally at least every 2/3 weeks. He travelled to London by overnight sleeper from Dundee via Edinburgh to Kings Cross. Frequently sleeper bookings could not be made until the last moment, because an emergency meeting had been called. He always managed to get a sleeper — until one occasion in 1952. Try as she might, his secretary was unable to obtain a berth for him, so he was booked onto the sleeper from Perth to Euston. He was furious and was still seething as he walked on to the platform at Perth Station. To his absolute disgust he found himself listed in the last berth on the last coach — "over the wheels" and with maximum lateral movement when the train was at speed. He demanded to see the Station Master and insisted he be moved to a berth nearer the middle of the train. This was simply not possible because the train was fully booked. He went to sleep still in a foul temper.

At 5.30 in the morning, his train, travelling at 70 m.p.h., ran into a stationary train at Watford Junction, following which a local train ploughed into the wreckage. There were many dead and injured in the so-called Watford Train Disaster. The only coach of the Perth Express left standing upright on the track was the last one! Every morning for the rest of his life, my father awoke with a fright at 5.30 a.m. Incidentally in November the following year, he was appointed President of the S.E.F. for the ensuing year.

Following his appointment as Chairman in 1963, he continued in his dual roles but decided to retire two years later. When he was appointed Shipyard Manager in 1932, the first ship delivered under his direction was Yard No. 316. In 1965, the last ship delivered under his direction was Yard No. 541. Not bad — 225 ships!

On the day of his retirement, I sent him the following telegram —
"Final trial completed satisfactorily. We have vacancies for skilled
men. Good rates, overtime etc. If interested, apply Shipyard
Director, Clydebank Shipyard".

CHAPTER 3

"FUN AND GAMES" WITH THE LABOUR FORCE

DUNDEE folk are sometimes described as being "thrawn" a term meaning laconic, stubborn and generally "difficult". Over the years, Caledon's labour force exhibited this trait on a daily basis. Even in the most critical of situations, the Glaswegian or the Geordie can see the humorous side — not so the Dundonian. My father had to cope with this difficult temperament which was hardly conducive to harmonious labour relations, even when things were running smoothly.

On one occasion, he was approached by a riveter's shop steward whom he knew well and who proceeded to deliver a heart-rending appeal for a "sub", (a "sub" or a subscription, is an advance of wages). The steward explained that his wife was sick and could not work and his kids needed new shoes but he could not afford to buy them. And so it went on. My father refused to give him a "sub", but instead pressed his own £5 note into the steward's hand, who accepted it with grateful thanks. Two days later, the same steward led the riveter's out on strike and this lasted a month! "Enough to destroy one's faith in human nature" — was my father's only comment.

An elderly plater's helper used to arrive at the yard on "pay day" with an unsealed and stamped envelope addressed to himself. Immediately after collecting his wages, he made his way from the yard to the nearest bus stop and en-route placed £1 of his wages into the envelope, sealed and posted it. The remainder of his wages were spent on drink on the Friday evening. Accordingly, he lived on

£1 until the next "pay day!" This might be described I suppose, as preparing for an early retirement!

Shipyards are not the easiest of places in which to supervise labour. The joiner's shop, plumber's shop and other trade shops were the exception. Elsewhere and particularly on board ships, the labour force was dispersed and located within various compartments. Management tried hard over the years to ensure that the labour force started and finished work at the proper time. They never succeeded. Nor did they succeed in eliminating tea-breaks. Managers and foremen were posted at strategic points all over the yard to try and keep the men at work — on ships gangways, at shed entrances and the like. The men however stopped work at 15 minutes before the end of the shift and slowly and silently made their way off the ships by various means. They joined their mates at ground level, who by 10 minutes before the end of the shift, were gathering force as they shuffled nearer to the main gate. Had they been permitted to reach the gate, there could well have been a serious accident.

Thus it came about that the last line of defence was the shipyard manager — my father, or in his absence, his assistant. At around 10 minutes to twelve o'clock, he would emerge from the office, in full view of a large crowd of workmen now some 50 yards from the gate. He would start to walk slowly towards them, while extracting his pocket watch from his waistcoat. The technique apparently was to try to catch somebody's eye in the front row, glare at him and keep walking forward. The front rank began to turn and move backwards, forcing their mates to do likewise. The whole crowd then retreated into the comparative warmth of the platers shed, where they remained until the whistle blew. This was a daily procedure and the tactic only had to fail once to cause serious injury to the shipyard manager. It never did.

One of the Caledon ships was undergoing "guarantee" dry docking in South Wales after having been in service for 12 months. My father travelled there to inspect and discuss the guarantee repair work with the relevant owners. He had completed this task and was making his way from the dry dock back to the offices, when he noticed men shuffling towards the main gate. The time was about 10 minutes before mid-day. He suddenly noticed that a few of the men in the crowd were riveters from Dundee. He could not see a sign of any shiprepair staff, so decided to "try it on". He turned round to face the men, caught the eye of one of the riveters and started "walking". It worked in South Wales too!

There was usually a strike in the Caledon yard sometime during the month of October. Normally one or another of the boilermaker trades walked out. They probably took it in turns. It was the potato-lifting season — or "tattie howking" as it was called. The caulker shop steward say would demand an immediate increase in wages for his department, based on wholly spurious grounds. When this was refused, the department withdrew its labour and made its way to the potato fields.

The boilermaker trades were dependent upon one another and because of the strict demarcation of work practised between each trade, the absence of one trade had an immediate impact on availability of work for the rest. In such situations, management frequently tried to carry on for a week or so, thereby creating a worse situation when the strikers returned. The imbalance then created could be very costly in both time and money.

In Caledon, when such situations arose, my father used to close the yard. Even joiners and plumbers were sent home. This action constituted a "lock-out" which was supposedly illegal. Illegal or not, this is what happened. My father claimed that it was usually the wives who forced their men to their senses and he may well have been right.

On one such occasion, again in October, the welders "took to the fields". The yard was duly closed. On December 15th or thereby, the welders returned to work with no increase in pay. Interviewed at his home by a local reporter, the welder's shop steward was quoted as saying "It wasn't that big - - - - - - Parker that got us back to work, it was Santa Claus"!

On his daily rounds of the yard, my father one day came across an employee idling. The man in question leapt to his feet and grabbed the nearest workpiece to hand — a small but heavy steelplate. This he placed on his shoulder and started walking purposefully towards the building berths. My father followed and after 15 minutes further perambulation the whistle blew for the lunch hour. The man dropped the plate and fled out of the gate, no doubt with an aching shoulder!

Of course a strike is a very serious matter. It is not only costly in terms of wasted man hours, but is very damaging to the company's reputation. Shipowners naturally do not take kindly to delays to their newbuilding caused by unconstitutional action by a group of trouble-makers. Despite the pressure applied by shipowners for the swift settlement of a dispute, I do not recall a single instance when a section of the labour force was awarded a pay rise as a result of strike action. As I was to learn myself some 25 years later, a strike by shipwrights immediately prior to a launch can be the most embarrassing of all. On a number of occasions, Caledon ship sponsors had to content themselves by naming, but not launching a ship.

While a strike was in progress and the yard closed, my father would come home in the evenings, pace round and round the dining room table, muttering "They've taken me on again. They've not won yet and they are not going to start now". Had the strikers known how worried he was they might well have held out longer.

In case however it may be thought that my father was on bad terms with all his employees, I should mention the occasion of his "retiral" dinner. The directors made him a presentation, but for some reason did not organise a farewell dinner. Instead, he organised and paid for his own. He told me afterwards that it was the only business dinner he had ever organised where he could have a free-hand in selecting those who would attend without regard to hurt feelings. The seating plan was indeed revealing. Apart from my mother, all the rest were employed at the yard. They included — one director, two managers, four foremen and two riveters and a labourer — all personally known to him over many years. They had themselves one tremendous party! He even laid on taxis afterwards for the riveters and the labourer!

The local paper carried a headline the next day — "The Hammer of Dundee retired yesterday after 49 years in shipbuilding".

CHAPTER 4

SHIPBUILDING PRIOR TO 1950

IN the early 1930s experimental work was being undertaken into electric-arc welding, to establish whether this process could be developed for shipbuilding production. Riveting was still the norm, mainly pneumatic but also hydraulic.

When America finally entered the War and started to unleash its huge industrial potential for wartime purposes, one of the prime requirements was for merchant ships, whose existing numbers had been decimated by U-boat attacks.

Using electric welding techniques extensively, great chunks of standard-type ships were assembled at sites all over the United States and converged on Kaiser's yards for final assembly. The ships were ultimately being turned out in days from the Kaiser establishments.

In the U.K. shipbuilding industry, some yards were ahead of others in replacing riveting by welding and in replacing "piecemeal" building by prefabrication. And certainly by 1955 most yards employed few if any riveters and by 1960 riveters had all but disappeared. So what was shipbuilding like prior to 1950?

For a start, hull construction techniques had changed little over four decades. Ship designs had changed. Marine engineering had undergone fundamental change, both in design and production with the advent of the marine diesel engine, which rendered the steam reciprocating engine redundant. In the higher power ranges diesel engines began to supplant the steam turbine.

But ships continued to be constructed as they had been for the past 30 or 40 years, in yards laid out for the purpose. The layout was characterised by a comparatively large number of building berths, with a set of steelwork shops which ran parallel to the river, across the head of these berths. Berth cranage consisted usually of fixed cranes (in a few cases, only fixed derricks), although some yards had travelling cranes, either on level crane tracks, or in a few cases, on overhead gantries. All were of light capacity — rarely over 15 tons safe working load.

Inside the steelwork shops, plate and bar handling was, by modern standards, positively antique. Some sheds boasted light overhead travelling cranes, but more frequently, hinged beams attached to the shed supports, on which were mounted pulley blocks, were the only means of lifting and transporting material.

In order to manhandle a plate measuring some 20 feet long and 7 feet wide into a shearing machine for example, a team of platers helpers was needed. Each wore a hessian apron and gloves and supported the plate at intervals along its length, while feeding it through the blades of the machine. The floor was normally of compacted soil and the dim overhead lighting almost obscured by the pall of smoke that permeated the sheds and which emanated from the plate and bar furnaces. Looking back on this picture today, it may seem remarkable that ships, big ships, could be constructed at all with such basic equipment.

This was by no means the view held at the time, although by 1950, the Swedish Shipbuilding Industry had already transformed steelwork construction of ships and U.K. shipbuilders were increasingly turning their eyes to these new methods and associated equipment.

Two factors, one geographic the other economic, had to be borne in mind. Geographically, most U.K. shipyards were located in heavily industrialised areas and their premises hemmed in on both sides and to the rear either by houses, factories, or other shipyards. Expansion, or at any rate, alterations to the layout, could only be undertaken within existing boundaries.

Economics could not be ignored. The slump of the late 20's lasted up to 1935 or even later in U.K. shipbuilding. Some yards were forced to close while others were on short-time. No reserves of capital were built up during this period for funding future investment in plant and machinery. In the case of the Caledon Yard at Dundee for example, no dividends had been paid to shareholders between the years 1932 and 1944. In 1944 the preference shareholders were paid twelve years dividend. This may indicate how financially weak certain yards had become due to the earlier depression.

In the meantime, Sweden was leading the world in shipbuilding production technology and no wonder. They had remained neutral throughout the War and on occasions German and British ships were being repaired side by side in their Gothenburg drydocks. And at a price. They had the money and had the available open spaces in which to layout new shipyards. West Germany too, assisted by U.S. dollars, was laying out new shipyards on the site of the ones destroyed by allied bombing. So too was Japan.

So the U.K. shipbuilding industry found itself, through no fault of its own, at a big disadvantage with many of its foreign competitors and had a lot of catching up to do. The early 50's saw this process begin, as profits made from 1946 onwards, were used to finance the investment.

But to return to shipbuilding prior to 1950, I have already briefly described the layout of berths and steelworking sheds. Mention must also be made of working hours, trade demarcation, methods of payment and supervision, to understand how it was possible to build a ship in such a comparatively short time with such elderly equipment.

The normal working week was one of 47 hours and this was only reduced to 44 hours in 1947. (It has long since been reduced to 40 or less).

All steelwork was undertaken by boilermakers and they set the pace for both levels of wage rates and conditions within the industry. Unlike the outfit trades — joiners, plumbers, electricians, fitters, coppersmiths, painters and others, who were able to find work in other industries, the boilermakers, who in any case represented the largest single union employed in the industry, were more dependent on shipbuilding and shiprepairing for their livliehood than their "outfit bretheren". They were and are a tough breed and in the times I speak of, worked under tough conditions. They had faced some harsh bosses over the years and even in 1950, could be "on the dole" on the spot, if work ran short.

Up to 1950 or thereby, most boilermakers were paid on

Piecework. This arrangement entailed a negotiation between management and the men concerned with prosecuting a certain "piece" of work. A fixed price would eventually be struck and thereafter, irrespective of circumstances (in theory), that fixed sum of money would be paid in full when the work was satisfactorily completed. It was normal for the squad of men to elect to be paid a "draw to account" each week, representing the squad's estimation of how long the work would take and dividing the fixed sum by the number of weeks involved. The money would be paid each week to the squad leader, who was then wholly responsible for disbursing it to his fellow tradesmen and semi and unskilled men in the squad. The squad leader hired and fired his own labour and woe betide the man who did not pull his weight.

Boilermakers were involved in every aspect of steel construction work, but maintained the strictest demarcation between each trade. Although such demarcation was taken to the most unrealistic limits and caused in the 1950's much adverse press publicity because of resulting strikes, the fact remains that part of the reason why demarcation was so jealously practised was because of the fear of unemployment. If for example, there was a shortage of work for shipwrights, but a demand for platers, the platers felt obliged to maintain their demarcation line with shipwrights, in case they too became unemployed.

Prior to 1950, foremen, particularly head foremen, exerted a key influence on all aspects of production and labour relations. They knew their men and they knew the job and they stood no nonsense.

A combination of longer working hours, piecework and good supervision, produced well-built ships from poor facilities and accounted for around 45% of World capacity. But things were beginning to change — for the worse. One major cause was not lack of work, but rather the reverse. The fear of unemployment, which had been a spur to production, had faded. The younger men, who had begun their apprenticeships after the War ended had never known "the dole".

Imperceptibly the work rate slackened. Demarcation if anything was practised even more assiduously despite its original "raison d'etre" having largely disappeared. Arguments erupted concerning piecework prices. Allowances were demanded for bad weather, plant breakdowns, shortage of material and a host of other items.

Some of these were reasonable, others were not. But when a piecework price list contains as many allowances as prices, it is no longer an incentive to produce goods. In addition, demands were made for a "fall-back" rate sometimes at a level as high as good piecework earnings.

Whereas previously the foremen, or head foremen, had dealt with such matters, management were gradually sucked into this arena. So it came about that managers took over all such discussions with shop stewards.

The two key elements to success, namely piecework and the key role of the foremen, were thus destroyed. Labour relations continued to deteriorate just at the point new plant was coming on stream, which hopefully would enable U.K. shipbuilders to catch up the leeway with Sweden and with the emerging West Germany and Japan. It was not to be however, as totally unrealistic manning scales and additional allowances were demanded for the operation of highly expensive cutting and welding equipment.

Thus began the decline of the U.K. shipbuilding industry as a World force, coincident with the growing might of the Japanese shipbuilding industry. Before the decade was out, not only was that country together with Sweden and West Germany, beginning to dominate World shipbuilding, but a host of other nations began to build ships of their own.

I started work in the industry in 1946 and by the time I had completed by apprenticeship and National Service, the deterioration noted above was already under way. It may be said that I joined the industry at an unpropitious time. Certainly my grandfather had started work when the industry was expanding at a great rate and Britain was the World's leading shipbuilder. In 1915 when my father began his career, U.K. shipbuilding was still a leading force. Compared to those scenarios, I certainly started with the industry in poorer shape. But despite its inexorable decline to the present day, the shipbuilding industry gave me huge job satisfaction, a lot of laughs and almost a "way of life".

CHAPTER 5

APPRENTICESHIP

IN 1946 no formal management training had been devised for the industry. There were two ladders to success — the first was Technical and the top rung of this particular ladder was the Technical Director. The second was Production and the top rung of this ladder was the Production Director. Before one could begin to climb either of these, convention demanded that a five year apprenticeship as a ship draughtsman had to be served.

Other career avenues existed other than those of pure ship-building. One could join a Classification Society like Lloyds Register or Bureau Veritas for example. Alternatively one might wish to join the Technical Department of one of the larger shipowners. Or one might hanker after consultancy or research work. But for these careers too, a prerequisite was training in the ship drawing office.

I started my apprenticeship with Alexander Stephen & Sons Ltd., of Linthouse, Glasgow, in September 1946 and a few weeks later began a 4 year Naval Architecture course at Glasgow University. October to March each year was spent at the University and the remaining part of the year at the yard. On completion of four years work, a further full year was spent at the yard to complete my apprenticeship.

Stephens was a medium-sized shipyard with its own Engine Works and Electrical Department. The company was one of the oldest shipbuilders in the U.K. and Sir Murray Stephen, the Chairman and his brother John, the Production Director, were the seventh generation of the family to run the business. The yard built naval ships including cruisers and destroyers and tended to specialise in refrigerated ships for the New Zealand Shipping Co. and other associated carriers of Australian and New Zealand meat. The yard also had a long association with Elder and Fyffes and built for these owners a number of fast and elegant banana boats. They also built intermediate sized passenger liners, including in 1929, the famous *Viceroy of India*, for P & O.

I didn't much like drawing office work and was I am sure an indifferent apprentice. A good draughtsman is neat, accurate and careful. I was none of these things and think I probably conformed to the draughtsman's motto — "when in doubt, leave out". It was with a great deal of surprise and relief that I was told that my second and third periods in the yard would be spent outside the drawing office. I was to be attached to tradesmen in various shipyard departments to learn at first hand how a ship was produced.

Meanwhile during the winter months I was toiling away at University, returning each night to my lodgings to study, except on Friday that is, which was reserved for beer followed by the second house of the famous Glasgow Empire — the so-called "graveyard of English comics".

Landladies come in different shapes and sizes, but in my experience they had one thing in common — a singular lack of imagination in the culinary arts. I ate blancmange for 3 or 4 nights each week for a period of some three years. The stuff has not passed my lips since.

The first two years of the four year Naval Architecture course was common to all other engineering courses within the Faculty. So one was being lectured in the company of civil, mechanical, chemical, electrical and mining engineering students. Only in the last two years did specialisation begin and in the final year one saw little of these other engineers. There were no less than 228 students within these various disciplines in the first year, but not many of these were Naval Architects. By the final year, fourteen students were being lectured in Naval Architecture. For one of these, a Greek, it was his third year in the final year. In the final year book of students, the following words were ascribed to him — "I aim to remain here for an immense period of time". I sat the final exams in

March/April 1950 and in June learned to my astonishment that I had passed.

It so happened that, on returning to Stephens in April, I was told to report to the design office. There I learned to my chagrin that despite my University training, I could not design a river tug, which was the subject of the yard's latest enquiry. I was soon to appreciate that the nature of the Naval Architecture course then in being at Glasgow University, was heavily slanted towards the theoretical. I am glad to note that all this changed for the better a long time ago.

My father had taught me that impatience was nearly a virtue and so looking back to my few years in a drawing office, I suppose it was inevitable that I was bawled out on a number of occasions for lack of accuracy — I always wanted to start the next drawing before bothering with the minutiae of the previous one. I had certainly no intention of remaining a draughtsman for all my working life, as most of the people at surrounding benches were destined to do. A number of elderly gentlemen were still drawing plans of immaculate conception at the age of 65 or 70 years of age. These plans were works of art and took months to complete. One such draughtsman drew the superstructure steel deck plans for all ships built at the yard. He was a nice old boy, ponderous in the extreme as well as being a creature of habit. To enliven the somewhat staid proceedings of the office, one bright spark of an apprentice bought a very life-like blob of ink (made of tin plate) from a local Joke Shop.

The latest work of art to emanate from Old Willie's hand — the Promenade Deck plating plan — was within a day or two of completion. Young Jimmy placed the blob midway along the plan and the office awaited with interest old Willie's return from his lunch. As usual, he walked slowly up the office to his bench while buttoning up his brown dust coat. Arriving at his bench, he then carefully unlocked his drawer full of drawing instruments and sat down on his stool. It was at this point he saw the ink. Extracting some blotting paper from his drawer, he carefully tried to mop up the ink but only succeeded in moving the blob along the plan. The whole office erupted into laughter. Willie was nae amused. The next day, Jimmy placed a real blob of ink on the plan, but Willie was not to be taken in a second time and swept the blob away with his hand. The Promenade Deck plating plan was very late indeed in being issued to the yard!

Stephens yard was one of the first to develop welding and prefabrication and were in the process of phasing out riveting. The steelwork facilities of the yard had been partially re-vamped to embrace these techniques, mainly in the provision of heavier berth cranage and a new prefabrication shed, where 30 ton steel units could be constructed. Directly across the River Clyde, Barclay Curle's Clydeholm Shipyard was still using traditional methods and I remember being greatly impressed by the speed of steel construction there compared to ours. But these were early days for prefabrication methods and there had to be a "learning curve".

My time spent in the various shipyard departments taught me how a ship was physically constructed and how each "steel trade" operated. But I think it taught me a lot more about human nature — in particular the Glaswegian nature. Crude but immensely kind might best sum up this nature. A simple story illustrates this to perfection.

It was "closing time" in one of Argyll Street's pubs on a Saturday night. Outside the pub, a Lascar employed on a U.K. ship berthed at Prince's Dock, Glasgow, having drunk his fill, was faced with a bewildering selection of different coloured tramcars and tramstops. Big Jimmy had also drunk his fill and reeling along Argyll Sreet, encountered the Lascar. In a flash of intuition he understood the problem. Swaying dangerously, he approached the Lascar —

"Hey, Ali, you aff a boat eh?" — No reply.

"Do you nae speak the lingo, Ali?" — Again no reply, but beseeching eyes.

"Dinna worry, Ali, ah'll get ye hame" — No response.

"Ye aff a Blue Funnel Boat, Ali?" — No reaction.

"Ye aff an Ellerman Boat, eh?" — instant reaction and vigorous nodding of the head.

"That's okay then, Ali, Ellerman Boats dock on the south side. You need a number 27 car — leave this tae me".

Ali was duly led unsteadily to a number 27 tram, while Jimmy with great presence of mind tore off a piece of a cigarette packet and writing briefly on it, handed the conductor the message while bundling Ali aboard.

In the flickering light and the swaying tramcar the conductor read the message — "Pit this b - - - - - aff at Govan".

A further example of Glasgow humour was illustrated by Bud

Neill, who for many years wrote a cartoon each evening in the *Glasgow Evening Citizen*, called, "Lobey Dosser". Lobey was portrayed as a bearded and floppy-hatted sheriff in Arizona who had constant run-ins with his villainous opponent, Rank Bajin. Lobey was usually to be found on his two-legged steed and Lobey's territory was frequently under attack by a tribe of Red Indians commanded by Big Chief Toffee Teeth, who spoke with a broad Glasgow accent. These evening articles were widely read and hugely appreciated by a discerning Glasgow public.

But Bud Neill also wrote poetry and one of his gems, to be recited at the first hint of frost, goes as follows:—

> *Winter's came*
> *The snow has fell,*
> *Wee Josie's nose is froze as well,*
> *Wee Josie's frosis nose is skintit.*
> *Winter's diabolic, Intit.*

On completion of my 5 year apprenticeship I was called up for National Service in the Army. Before leaving I was sent for by Mr. John Stephen, who very kindly offered to employ me on completion of my 2 year National Service. In view of the trouble that he and the company had taken to widen the scope of my apprenticeship, I felt obliged and was indeed grateful to accept.

CHAPTER 6

SERVICE INTERLUDE

I was instructed to report to No. 2 Training Battalion, R.E.M.E. at Honiton in Devon. There, after a few weeks' training, I had the temerity to apply for a commission. Some 30 others did likewise. For the next 2/3 months, we were subjected to some fairly rough treatment including various tests and interviews, before 16 of us were sent for a 3 day physical and mental examination by the War Office Selection Board near Andover in Hampshire. By sheer good fortune and a great deal of bravado 5 of us cleared this hurdle. Within another month I was installed at Eaton Hall, near Chester, as an officer cadet.

By this time I was getting used to army life and at Eaton Hall, we were treated courteously, except at drill. Twice each day we were drilled by extremely fierce Warrant Officers and Colour Sergeants from the Coldstream and Grenadier Guards. I am reminded of the Avis motto — "We try harder!" The training was roughly based on Sandhurst methods with lectures interspersed with assault courses and drill. Imperceptably everyone became fitter and fitter. The 16 week course ended with a 10 day "battle camp" on Dartmoor near Okehampton.

In June 1952, I was commissioned as a 2nd Lieutenant in R.E.M.E. Various short courses followed and finally in September I received my official "posting". I am afraid that I cannot report being sent anywhere exciting like Hong Kong, or to Korea (where we were fighting), or even to B.A.O.R. in Germany. But the job I got was very unusual, so unusual that many army personnel had never heard of it. It was called Water Transport. I was posted to No. 45 Water Transport Company, R.E.M.E., Menai Bridge, Anglesey, as the workshop officer. The set-up was interesting.

Sixteen launches were under the command of the Royal Army Service Corps. (R.A.S.C.) — in the shape of one elderly captain, a young 2nd Lieutenant, a sergeant and a driver. Manning the boats were local sailors and engineers who were attached to the R.A.S.C. but wore Merchant Navy style uniforms. The H.Q. was located on a tiny island off Menai Bridge itself. My workshops were entirely separate and located almost directly under the famous Telford Bridge, some half a mile away from H.Q. They consisted of a jetty, alongside of which was a workshop, store and two tiny offices. Next to these was a concrete slipway complete with hand winch.

I was under the command of the R.A.S.C. captain for discipline only. For all other matters — technical, stores, repairs etc. I was under the command of a Lieutenant-Colonel based at Kingston Upon Thames. I was interviewed by him prior to my posting. I never saw him again.

The boats were of various sizes and classes, all of wood construction, mostly of double-diagonal planking. The largest class were 69 feet in length, powered by no less than three huge Thornycroft petrol engines, which drove the boats at some 28 knots. There were two of these together with two at 68 feet, two at 45 feet and various smaller craft including one open harbour launch. They were used mainly for towing targets off the coast of North Wales at Towyn, off West Wales near Aberdovey and South Wales near Barry. Land-based gunners fired at the moving targets. Occasionally the 69 footers relieved the air-sea rescue boat based at Holyhead. Two slow diesel-engined boats carried fresh water to batteries located in the Mersey estuary.

The Army is required to carry out an inspection on each vehicle once a month — the so-called 406 inspection. Similarly the boats were subjected to a 407 inspection each month. This was my job, together with ensuring that all 16 craft were maintained in good repair. Five of these however were in mothballs, so effectively only 11 boats had to be looked after.

I found myself in charge of 14 civilian Welshmen — including a foreman, a storeman, 2 shipwrights and various turners, drillers and welders. A funny lot and I mean funny peculiar!

For repair work exceeding a cost of £1,000 per week, the work would normally be contracted out to one of three local boatyards and an inspector sent up from Kingston on Thames to supervise the work. I soon discovered that the three local boatyards were contemptuous of War Department work from March until October (the yachting season), but would fall over themselves to take any work in the winter months. Not long after arriving, our harbour launch was returned from one of these yards after a lengthy stay, ostensibly for dry rot repairs and engine overhaul. I had a look at it and was able to sink a 12-inch screwdriver up to the handle in a number of the timbers behind the small galley stove. I suspected that the appointed inspector was casual in his approach to work. In any event, I hoped privately that I could in the future undertake such repairs at our own workshop, but this required upgrading our hand winch from 5 tons S.W.L. up to 12½ tons S.W.L. This work we undertook ourselves and when completed we had a trial run to see if we could haul one of our 68 footers up the slipway. We managed it, but not before all 14 employees were straining on a greatly extended winch handle! Thereafter we slipped all our own boats and saved the War Office some money. In the process I became very unpopular with the foreman shipwright of the boat builder in question.

I enjoyed most of my time at Menai Bridge. Being such a tiny Army unit there was no Officers Mess. I was billeted in a local guest house named, "Ye Olde Tea Gardens" and was taken in hand by the most delightful couple — Jones "Policeman" and his wife Florrie. He had retired from the Police Force in Tregaron in West Wales. They were extremely kind to me and fed me like a fighting cock. Apart from these two and their family, I found the locals very peculiar. For example, approaching the Liverpool Arms in the village, I could hear everyone speaking in English but as soon as I opened the door, Welsh was spoken. After 12 months in North Wales, my "time was up" and I was more than ready to return to shipbuilding and in particular, to Stephen's shipyard.

Two years earlier, the production management set-up at Stephens was generally similar to that in most other yards. The production director was Mr. John Stephen and reporting to him was a general manager, under whom were a steel manager and an outfit manager. Three or four assistant managers took charge of individual ships as they approached launch stage.

On returning to Stephens in October 1953, a transformation had taken place in the supervision of shipyard production. A new face had appeared in the role of production director and he had proceeded to build a great pyramid of management. To mix up my metaphors a little, I found myself at the base — alone — as a trainee manager! I was given numerous trifling jobs to undertake while gazing with envy at those given responsibility for the charge of one ship. The salary was lousy, but what was infinitely worse was that I was not getting any experience of real management.

I grew daily more impatient and frustrated. After a year or so, my father heard of a vacancy for an assistant manager at Lithgows Ltd., Port Glasgow, some 20 miles down the river. I jumped at the chance of applying for the position and was interviewed and engaged to start at the beginning of January 1955. I had married in April of the previous year and set up home in a small house in Glasgow. But with no car we could not continue to live there and so we moved to Greenock 2 weeks after starting my new job.

CHAPTER 7

LITHGOWS LIMITED

I had learned something about how ships were built in my early days in Dundee. My apprenticeship at Stephen's taught me more and in some detail. But Lithgows was the place where I finally came to assume real responsibility at the age of 26.

I knew something of Lithgows, because of course my grandfather had worked there. I knew for instance, that they operated 2 shipyards (a mile or so apart) in Port Glasgow. The larger one — Kingston Yard was the one that employed me. I also knew that other major and minor companies, mainly located in the West of Scotland, formed with the two Port Glasgow shipyards, the Lithgow Group of Companies. Lithgows retained for example, a financial interest in Fairfield's large yard at Govan, as well as in David Rowan & Co. Ltd., the Marine Engineers.

I also knew that Lithgows used to be known as builders of "bread and butter" ships — the tramp steamers as they were called. They built standard ships "on spec" during the slump of the early 1930's. They sold for £55,000 each!

When I joined the company I felt among friends immediately. There was no complex management structure — just a simple and direct chain of command. Alexander White was the Managing Director and Ross Belch the Director and General Manager. David Cunningham was the Director and Company Secretary. These three formed the executive members of Lithgow's Ltd., Board. Below Board level there was a shipyard manager in each yard, each with two assistant managers. In the offices there was a chief draughtsman and his assistant, a buyer and a cashier. That was the management.

I arrived on a cold January morning with snow on the ground. On the berths stood a partially-built oil tanker also covered in snow. Lithgows then built ships from the stern "up" — the travelling 25 ton crane moving backwards up the centre of the berth. The ship was at this point erected up to the forepeak bulkhead.

The yard manager told me that this was my ship and that I was to be responsible for it through to completion. It was the *Kaldfonn*, an 18,000 ton deadweight tanker for Sigval Bergesen of Stavanger. It looked enormous. I had never drawn a plan for let alone set foot upon an oil tanker before.

I was very fortunate in that David Rowan & Co. Ltd., the makers of the ship's turbines, were running very late in delivery. They had at the time, a huge order book and had given in good faith some optimistic delivery promises. I say fortunate for me, because it gave me more time to try to get to grips with my new job.

I was informed of the starting and finishing times and the lunch break. It was stressed that no tea-breaks were permitted at any time. Before leaving the yard manager's office to go on board the ship, he said — "Make sure no-one goes down the gangway before 2 minutes to twelve—the whistle blows at twelve". I climbed the gangway on to the deck. The ship seemed deserted. At this point in construction, the superstructure was not in place — just the flat upper deck, perforated by a number of large oval holes, where later the oil-tight hatches would be fitted.

I climbed down through one of these openings onto the stage planks, some 3 feet below the underside of the deck and spaced some 18 inches apart. Looking down, there was a sheer drop to the bottom of the ship some 40 feet or so below.

Suddenly I thought I smelled something cooking. Looking aft, I saw 3 workmen sitting on the staging, backed against the far bulkhead, enjoying hot tea and toast! There was no way out for them, but my problem was worse. How was I to duck under a deep beam which was positioned between them and me and at the same time not fall off the staging? With great difficulty was the answer. When I finally confronted them, they calmly continued eating their snack until I informed them who I was and that they were now ex-employees! In due course I duly reported all this to the Head Foreman concerned, who in turn reported to the Yard Manager. He persuaded me, later in the morning, that dismissal was too heavy a punishment and proposed instead 3 days suspension without pay. I could not have known of course, that the 3 men concerned were among the most productive in the entire yard!

Back on board it was 11.45 a.m. and I stood alone on the snow-covered deck. A workman appeared from an oil tank and made to walk down the gangway. He announced he needed to go to the toilet. I told him he could wait for another 10 minutes and he disappeared back into the tank. For the next 10 minutes, various workmen approached, each offering a different reason for wanting off the ship. None of them went down the gangway. At 2 minutes to twelve, I walked down the gangway but no workmen were to be seen, nor were any to be seen when the whistle blew at mid-day. All had apparently clambered down the shipside staging while I was still on deck! But honour was satisfied and what a first morning!

When the ship was launched, as the manager in charge, it was my duty to be on board. It felt like a roller coaster for the 25 seconds it took for the ship to get afloat. Then it was a tow up to Glasgow for the installation of the main machinery. It took nearly 6 months thereafter before the ship was ready for trials and handover, due to the engine delay. I was never to have the luxury of such a timescale again and I hope I took full advantage of it by trying to master my job.

I cannot imagine a more exciting prospect than being in charge of a ship fitting-out. At that time 15 quite separate shipyard trades were involved in shipbuilding, not to mention the semi and unskilled workers. To this had to be added a host of sub-contractors installing everything from the Radio room to the insulation of bulkheads, from the tiling of bathrooms to the installation of the rigging. All of this conglomorate required to be organised in such a way as to meet the price allowed in the estimate and the delivery date contracted to the owner.

Lithgows had at that time no Planning Department. Work scheduling, production control and the like, were not in place. The assistant manager was a "walking planner". It was a busy, not to say hectic lifestyle. Overtime was worked on a minimum of 2 nights per week and every Sunday. This was necessary to try to make inroads into a bulging order book — some 5 years work or more!

The last 2 or 3 weeks before trials and handover were even more nerve-tingling, as the days went slipping by with so much work still left to do. It reached a crescendo on the night before the trial. Lithgows considered that it was an assistant manager's duty to be at work all through the night supervising the so-called finishing touches. Just as one can remember every detail of one's first car, I can recall in great detail the events leading up to the trials of this my first ship.

The *Kaldfonn* was lying at Stobcross Quay in Glasgow and due to sail on the tide at 6.00 a.m. on the following day. Under the command of tugs, she would make her way downriver, anchor at the Tail-of-the-Bank and await the arrival of the owner's and builder's trial party at 9.00 a.m. The plan then was for all trials to be completed by about nightfall, followed hopefully by handover. Thereafter the ship would sail the following morning on her maiden voyage.

The plan seemed fair enough, but what of the ship herself at 9.00 p.m. on the previous evening. A scene of almost total chaos met the eye on every part of the vessel. Nothing could be seen of the upper deck. It was piled high with stage planks removed from the oil tanks, engine and boiler rooms and elsewhere. Great heaps of rubbish, ladders, steel plates and bars lay everywhere. As one pile was removed ashore by crane, another two took its place. Welders were still at work and so were other boilermakers still installing bits and pieces. In theory it was final paint coating time! Power cables lay everywhere, alongside gas bottles. I tried to be everywhere at once, trying hard to see some "light at the end of the tunnel". By midnight, it was if anything worse on deck, but improving slightly below decks. The oiler arrived alongside to pump the fuel oil aboard required for the trials. I had already informed Rowan's engineers that this oil was to be pumped into the forward deep tank and not into the double bottom oil fuel tanks in the Engine Room. This arrangement ensured a slight trim by the stern needed for trials. I saw that the oiler was safely moored and took no further notice of it.

Cleaning up continued at a frenetic pace and by 5.00 a.m. as daylight was breaking (and with one hour to departure), I could now see large areas of the upper deck clear, although I did not care to look too long at the debris on the Clyde Navigation Trust's jetty!

Just after 5.00 a.m. the voice of David Rowan's senior manager sounded in my ear — "The pilot is on board and he won't sail the vessel. He says the trim is excessive". I looked forward and aft along the sloping deck. We must have been floating with a trim of some 20 feet by the stern! It was quite obvious what had happened. The engineers had pumped all the fuel oil into the aft tanks and gradually, over a few hours, the trim had increased to its now unacceptable level.

The ship's captain, sound asleep in his cabin throughout the noise and chaos surrounding him, was awoken by myself and informed of the position. He had always refused to allow us to pressure test the cargo oil valves in the oil tanks because he believed that they should only be tested in clean salt water, not available in Glasgow's docks. I had to inform him that I proposed to open the sea valve in the Pump Room and flood No. 1 cargo tanks — port, starboard and centre, near the bow. So much for pollution!

This procedure was set in motion and in less than 30 minutes, the ship was satisfactorily trimmed. At 5.45 a.m. the pilot announced that he could now sail the vessel. We were on our way down river at exactly 6.00 a.m. on a fine September morning. On our slow passage towards the Tail-of-the-Bank, the remaining rubbish was unceremoniously dumped overboard — bits of steel, welding rods, timber of all shapes and sizes and paint drums by the dozen. All a punishable offence by the River Authority! At 6.30 a.m., we started painting the decks and by 9.00 a.m. it was 90% complete — plenty of spirit mixed in with the paint to dry it quickly. As our foreman painter put it — "The man who invented white spirit ought to have got a bloody knighthood".

The tug brought the trial party out to the ship from Gourock Pier. As I stood at the top of the accommodation ladder waiting to greet them, I felt a deep glow of satisfaction. The ship was duly handed over and sailed the next day in ballast to uplift her first cargo of oil. (*See illustration*).

For me it was on to another partly-built ship on the building berth — this time a straightforward ore carrier. I felt a lot less worried than I had been 6 months previously. Over the next few years, a number of ships followed. By this time, I was really enjoying the work, despite the long hours and the fact that I lost half a stone in weight during the few weeks before delivery of each ship.

MV *Kaldfonn* on trials, September 1955.

One of these ships was noteworthy for a number of reasons. She was a pilgrim ship called the *Saudi* and built for the Mogul Line of Bombay. She was specially designed to carry Moslems from India to Jeddah. They then went overland to Mecca. I believe it is an ambition of all Moslems to make this trip and for the Mogul Line I think, it was probably a very profitable business.

The *Saudi* was laid out for 2 classes of pilgrim, the very rich — and the rest. The former were berthed in elegant wood-panelled cabins within the superstructure. The latter — all 987 of them, were accommodated below the decks. Steel beds, each large enough to hold some 20 or so pilgrims, could be hinged into an upright position against the shipsides when not in use — that is to say, when the ship was carrying cargo outwith the "pilgrim season".

The toilet facilities were crude in the extreme. Four sets of W.C.'s and urinals were located at the four corners of the superstructure at upper deck level — a total of 48 of each item. Each set of 12 was designed to be flushed automatically every 2 minutes. Washing facilities consisted only of cold saltwater taps on deck — outside each toilet area! Below decks, were 9 small galleys where the pilgrims did their own cooking! While all this was unusual enough, what made the fitting-out of the ship memorable for me was the raw condition of the ship at launch and the imperative need to have the ship in Bombay for the start of the "pilgrim season" some 4 months later.

Saudi was built in Lithgow East Yard. As the end of 1955 approached, this yard had 3 ships all approaching launch stage. This in itself was very unusual and was probably caused by a delay in one or more of the ships earlier in the year. In any event, it was decreed that all 3 ships were to be launched within a period of 3 weeks.

Because of the yard's excessive workload, all the steelwork for the *Saudi* had been subcontracted to Fairfield's at Govan — some 20 miles away. Thereafter lorry loads of prepared plates and sections poured into the East Yard over a period of months. But because the yard was so busy with the other 2 vessels, this material, lying all over the yard, was largely ignored. When work started in earnest on the *Saudi*, it was immediately discovered that the material was totally mixed up — double bottom floors were stowed with main bulkheads, superstructure and so on.

Somehow or another, the steelwork was put together and the ship launched in the last few days of December, but in what a condition! The main bulkheads were not even connected to the hull! The upper deck plating was held together not by rivets, but by service bolts. The superstructure was still lying in piles of plates and sections in the East Yard. I joined the ship immediately after the New Year Holiday in early January 1956 and surveyed this scene. It was a great challenge and I received a lot of help from those above and below me.

The real problem was that outfitting just had to commence before basic steelwork was anything like complete. To add to the difficulties, it was not a large ship — only 395 feet in length. In the native galleys for example, there wasn't room to swing a riveter! But try to swing him we did. I recall a galley range being fitted, while hot rivets were being driven into the deck immediately overhead!

Everything went wrong as we struggled towards completion. Both masts were in place with the derricks rigged. With few men working on Saturday mornings, it was adjudged a good time to test the derricks. When the test load was applied, the masts bent! It was then discovered that the masts had been designed for 5 ton derricks, but in fact they were 10 tons! Both masts had to be unstepped and repaired.

Finally all tests on board were nearing completion — electrical, ventilation, main engine dock trials etc. The ship was due to sail in 48 hours, with frantic efforts being made to clean up the ship. I thought we could just manage it, except for one thing. Try as we might, we could not get the automatic flushing system in the toilets to operate properly. In a row of 12 urinals for example, we had numbers 1-3 drenched, numbers 4-9 about right and numbers 10-12 with no water! Or vice-versa! Mr. Shanks arrived on board personally.

Captain Morini, in command of the ship was an amusing and understanding man. He said to me — "This is real bad luck after all the effort that has been expended in trying to meet the delivery date. I would sail the ship even if the emergency steering wasn't working. But these toilets — I am carrying a thousand pilgrims and they are regular in their habits! I must have the toilets working properly". Eventually the toilets were fixed and the ship sailed, I think 24 hours late and these anxious pilgrims in Bombay were duly uplifted. (*See illustration*).

The *Athelcrest* was a modest size tanker of some 12,000 tons deadweight. She was constructed not to carry oil, but molasses as well as caustic soda. This dual role required the ship to be equipped with 2 sets of cargo tank piping and valves and for a tanker of this period she was really quite complex.

During the time the ship's hull was under construction, a steel inspector from Athel Line was in attendance. As usual, I joined the ship a month or two before the launch and work was proceeding quite normally. Immediately after the launch, the hull inspector was joined by the chief engineer appointed to the vessel. It was unusual for the ship's chief engineer to stand by for the whole of the outfitting period, but this was no ordinary chief engineer! This was Hughie Milne, aged around 65, a bachelor and Greenock born and bred. He spent most of his working life with the Athel Line and what he didn't know about molasses tankers wasn't worth knowing.

He was the ideal man for taking care of the owner's interests. He knew the detailed layout of each compartment and in many cases the plans issued from the Drawing Office were ignored in deference to this man's knowledge of the systems. He was a "card" and could be and frequently was rude and overbearing but with a huge sense of humour. He literally had a story for every occasion and I got on famously with him.

One evening he invited my wife and me to his bachelor flat. In the corner of the room stood a cocktail cabinet, filled to capacity with spirits of every description. Not for him, he liked his whisky. He asked my wife what she wanted to drink and she asked for a martini. Hughie immediately shot her a glance and said, — "It's a dangerous drink a martini". We both looked puzzled. Hughie continued —

"Beware of the wily martini,
Only have two at the most,
Have three you'll be under the table,
And four you'll be under your host".

The *Harmattan* was a cargo ship of some 10,000 tons deadweight built for J. & C. Harrison Ltd., of London. She was to be the last ship I would fit out. There was nothing particularly special or complex about the vessel, but unfortunately the steel hatch covers would not fit the ship's hatch openings.

The pilgrim/cargo vessel SS *Saudi*, April 1956.

The covers had as usual been subcontracted to a local firm of fabricators. The covers were carefully measured by us and found to be inaccurate in all cases and so we demanded they be returned to the factory and corrected. This was a big job for a modest sized contractor. In due course they were returned but still would not fit. We eventually had to modify a number of the steel hatch openings to try to make them fit the covers.

The ship's delivery was delayed by a month but the owner was very forbearing. Eventually all was well and the ship completed after running successful sea trials. The vessel was chartered to carry grain from a U.S. Gulf port to Russia and was to proceed fully ballasted to the loading port. No. 3 hold, immediately forward of the Engine Room was a deep tank, which could contain 1,200 tons of salt water ballast. The tank could alternatively be used for grain cargoes. In preparation for her maiden voyage this deep tank was filled with salt water and the deep tank hatch covers closed down.

On the night before the ship's departure, I decided to take a last look around the vessel. The crew who had been accommodated ashore were due to arrive early next morning and as I went on board the ship seemed deserted. I knew however that there would be an engineer foreman on watch in the Engine Room. I walked slowly through the 'tween decks admiring the gleaming paintwork in the glare of the ship's lighting. Suddenly I thought I smelled oil fuel. The odour became stronger as I proceeded further aft and in No. 3 'tween deck the smell was overpowering. I was standing on top of the deep tank, supposedly filled with salt water. I suspected the worst and quickly located the engineer foreman at the bottom of the Engine Room.

I told him that I thought oil had found its way into the deep tank and that I wanted a manhole cover removed to check the situation. Ten minutes later the cover was removed and sure enough oil was present. How much we could not tell, because of course the oil would float on top of the salt water. The cover was replaced and I asked the foreman, whom I knew well, to say nothing of this occurrence to a living soul. I went ashore and phoned my boss.

I suggested that only two courses of action were open to us, both pretty unacceptable. The first was to do and say nothing. The ship had after all been handed over and we could allege when the oil contamination had been discovered, that the ship's engineers must have been responsible. Alternatively, we could own up to the situation, in which case the tank's contents would have to be pumped out into a sludge vessel and thereafter the tank "steamed out", allowed to cool and then cleaned down by hand, probably 2 or 3 times. In this event of course, the ship would lose her charter due to the delay.

There was no choice really and the ship was delayed a further 10 days. The problem in cleaning was that as the sludge level in the tank fell, oil residue covered the entire surface of the tank. The tank had to be cleaned 3 times before it was pronounced satisfactory.

By March 1960, I had fitted out 8 ships and Ross Belch decided that the time had arrived to take me off production for a spell, in order that I might have an insight into the realms of design and estimating. He himself had spent a year or so in this department prior to his becoming Director & General Manager. I duly reported to the Design & Estimating Office and began a fascinating and amusing 18 months. There I learned a great deal about fixing a ship's dimensions, based on the owners basic requirements for deadweight, cubic capacity, speed and draught limitations. It was very interesting indeed to develop the lines of the ship and from these draw the General Arrangement plan.

Ross Belch took a close personal interest in both design and estimating and frequently took part in discussions about all aspects of these subjects. It was very democratic in that everyone felt free to express strongly held opinions on various matters affecting design and of prices being worked into an estimate. The atmosphere was always very friendly. It had to be, because we were all cooped up in a small office and worked very long hours indeed.

When the design and estimate were completed a ship's specification had to be written. More discussion, banter and argument followed. Finally a tender letter was written and Ross Belch usually drafted this himself enduring constant interruptions during the process.

It was around this time also that it was decided that I should represent Lithgows on the Conference and Claims Committee of the Clyde Shipbuilders Association, so that I could begin to have an insight into wage rates, wage claims and trade union practice.

CHAPTER 8

THE CLYDE SHIPBUILDERS ASSOCIATION

THERE was in being within the industry a procedure for the settlement of disputes and it operated thus.

If a dispute arose within a yard, the matter would be discussed initially between the shop stewards concerned and the foreman. If the matter remained unresolved the shop stewards met the yard management. If this failed to produce a solution, a Yard Conference was convened at which the shop stewards and their local trade union delegate would meet the yard management accompanied by an official of the local Shipbuilders Association. Formal notes were taken and the meeting normally took place in the yard concerned. If the dispute was still unresolved, a Local Conference was arranged. This took place in the offices of the Local Shipbuilders Association and was attended by, on the union side, one or more trade union delegates (frequently 3 or 4) and a number of shop stewards. On the employers side, a committee of shipbuilders, drawn from a number of yards on the river concerned attended this meeting together with staff of the local Association. A shorthand writer was present.

If all this procedure had still not resolved the issue, the matter was referred to National Level, at a Central Conference. At such a meeting, held in the offices of the Shipbuilding Employers Federation in London, the trade unions were represented normally by the President and/or General Secretary of the union concerned, a number of District Delegates and some shipyard representatives. The employers were represented by a committee of senior shipbuilders drawn from all over the U.K. together with the permanent officials of the Federation and the local Shipbuilders Association. Again a shorthand writer was present. Perhaps not surprisingly, no other machinery was available for the settlement of disputes within the shipbuilding industry other than Arbitration, which was rarely used.

The Clyde Shipbuilders Association had their offices at 105 West George Street, Glasgow and the path to that door came to be well worn by me over the next 10 years. The Association employed a permanent staff of 3 plus typists. Bill Dawson was the Secretary and a lawyer by profession. He was quite masterly at his job and had a mind like a needle. He wasn't averse to "a wee dram" and even when displaying three sheets to the wind, remained as sharp as a tack. His assistant Bill McFadyen, gave the appearance of being very staid and thoroughly correct. In fact he had a wonderful sense of humour, bags of commonsense and was as at home with the union people as was his boss. The third member of the staff tended to be involved in the more minor disputes and undertook a good deal of office work. In 1960 the third member was Teddy Taylor, now M.P. for Southend. He did a good job at West George Street.

The Clyde Shipbuilders Association each year appointed a President, a Vice-President and an Executive Committee. The persons elected were all senior shipbuilders in local shipyards, mainly at Managing Director or Production Director level. The Association also appointed each year, persons to the Conference and Claims Committee. This Committee consisted of shipbuilders, mainly at shipyard manager level.

Bill Dawson told me that when he was first appointed Secretary of the Association, my grandfather was a senior member of the Conference and Claims Committee. Apparently on one occasion the Committee had listened to a very complex claim involving the Clyde Riveters piecework price list. The delegates droned on and were finally asked to retire. The Committee could come to no concensus and so with some exasperation the Chairman decided to call for a vote around the table.

Regrettably, soon after the delegates had started to present their claim, my grandfather had nodded quietly off to sleep. The Chairman nudged him awake and enquired as to his vote. He was informed — "I regret Chairman that I have not listened to much of the case, but as a matter of sheer principle, my answer is NO!"

This committee normally was involved with local conferences and as stated earlier, it was to this Committee that I was appointed. I received only one piece of advice before setting out for my first meeting — "Keep your mouth shut and your ears open". I don't believe I said a single word for six months.

I was fascinated by the discussions that took place. Before a particular case was heard, our Committee would be given an excellent resumé of the dispute by the Association staff and the yard management concerned. The union delegation would then be invited into the Committee room to present their claim, followed normally by a discussion across the table. When the discussion ran out of steam, the Chairman of the Committee would request an adjournment and the union delegation then retired while the committee considered its verdict.

I learned how relatively easy it was to settle someone else's dispute, but how difficult it was to accept the Committee's verdict for one of your own. I learned too why on occasion certain employers sitting around the table seemed quite agreeable to concede all or part of a claim. The reason frequently was because they were facing a similar claim at their own establishment, but wanted the excuse for a settlement at another yard.

I also began to appreciate that not all the good guys were employers and not all the bad guys were union delegates. Far from it. A number of the union delegates were thoroughly nice people who were only doing the job they were paid to do — namely, without unduly risking employment prospects, negotiate the highest wage rates and best conditions possible.

I began to comprehend that usually the tougher the union delegate, the more certain one could be that he would ensure that any deal struck would be forced through and honoured, regardless of how difficult it might be to sell to his members.

I marvelled at how some employers were loathe to accept any solution to their problem and seemed unwilling to offer any solution themselves. I came to understand that such employers were under strict orders from their Managing Director. We naturally were all under guidance from our superiors and while some were held on a light rein, others were rigidly tied.

When I first joined the Committee, there were no less than 23 firms represented on the Association. They included shipyards and shiprepair yards from the Upper Clyde to the Lower Clyde at Greenock and Port Glasgow and down as far as Troon. Quickly I got acquainted with my opposite numbers, in yards up and down the river and at the Association's Annual Dinner and again at their Annual Cocktail Party, I gradually came to know the managing directors of these establishments.

Humour was appreciated across the negotiating table, while sarcasm was anathema to the delegates. I discovered to my intense amusement that trade union delegates, particularly when in "full flow" presenting a claim, frequently committed some wonderful malapropisms. On one occasion I recall, I was faced with a dispute involving stagers — the men who erect and dismantle the stage planks. The delegate concerned was warming to his theme and finally burst out — "You'd get on a damn sight better if you invested in some tubercular scaffolding!"

In the early 60's shipbuilders were trying very hard to eliminate demarcation, particularly between the boilermaker trades, by the introduction of interchangeability and flexibility between these trades. This suggestion was at first fiercely resisted by boilermakers union delegates all over the country. In one heated exchange on this subject at West George Street, one boilermaker's delegate interrupted to say — "You'se all must be joking, if ya want changeability and interflexibility for 3d./hour!"

I hope I learned a good deal about labour relations from the deliberations of the Conference and Claims Committee. I certainly got to know the local union officials and this was to be of greater importance in future years.

After some 15 months or so in the Design and Estimating office, I was appointed Assistant General Manager of Lithgows Ltd. The shipyard managers at both Kingston and East Yards were very experienced and capable men, some 25 years my senior. Yet in theory at any rate, I was now their superior. The situation was akin to the relationship between a subaltern and a Regimental Sergeant Major in the Army.

This reminds me of the occasion when, having just been commissioned at Officer Cadet School near Chester, I entered the tailor's shop adjoining the barrack square. My object was simple but pleasureable — I came to purchase two pairs of "pips" for my shoulder straps. Savouring the moment, I made my request known.

The little Jewish tailor, totally unimpressed, pushed a large hat box across the counter, containing pips of every conceivable colour. I selected two sets of the navy blue required for R.E.M.E. I didn't hear the door open behind me, nor sense the approach of the huge figure of the R.S.M. I cupped the four pips in my hand at which point an unmistakeable voice close to my ear said, — "Ten a bloody penny, Sir!"

I think I appreciated my new situation and made it my business to try to operate in such a way that would not deliberately flout my new-found authority. Since both men were extremely busy looking after hull construction work, I assumed the mantle of overlord for outfitting of ships from both yards. In addition I was given the task of handling all the correspondence in relation to guarantee repairs as well as organising the necessary work to be put in hand.

A year or so passed, by which time I had spent nearly 8 years at Lithgows, had hugely enjoyed the work and the Company. I had also made many friends in the area. Without warning late one night, I received a telephone call. The unmistakable voice of John Rannie, the Shipyard Director of John Browns of Clydebank was on the other end. The substance of the call was that since he was shortly to be promoted Managing Director, he wondered whether I would be interested in the job of Shipyard Director. I consulted my father and discussed the pros and cons, including my possible future at Lithgows. The following week I accepted the offer.

CHAPTER 9

JOHN BROWN & CO. (CLYDEBANK) LTD.

I entered an entirely different world of shipbuilding when I joined Brown's in February 1963. The shipyard formed part of John Brown & Co. Ltd., whose registered offices were in Sheffield. A large number of companies made up the group, which included machine-tool makers, manufacturers of mining equipment, railway coach builders and many other products. The shipyard was the largest company within the Group. A number of main board directors were also on the shipyard board. The Chairman of the both Group and shipyard was Lord Aberconway.

The shipyard is situated on a bend of the River Clyde at its confluence with the River Cart and looked out across fields to the South. In 1963, it was one of the largest shipyards in the U.K., in terms of both employment and size of vessels built. The company had its own large engine works, located immediately behind the shipyard and had licences to build Pametrada Steam Turbines and Sulzer and Doxford Diesel Engines up to the highest powers.

The shipyard consisted of the East Yard with four building berths and the West Yard with two building berths. The two yards were separated by the fitting-out basin, which was set at right angles to the river and was over 1,000 feet in length and some 800 feet in width. Each yard had its own steelworking facilities. Set around the head of the outfit basin were the large outfitting shops for joiners, plumbers, electricians, engineers, painters etc. When I joined the company the shipyard alone employed some 4,000 staff and workers.

The shipyard was of course, world-renowned as the builders of the *Queen Mary* and the *Queen Elizabeth*, as well as other famous passenger liners for the Cunard Line such as *Acquitania* and *Lusitania*, as well as the *Empress of Britain* for Canadian Pacific. The yard had also constructed many of the largest Royal Navy Vessels including the battleship HMS *Barham*, the battle cruiser HMS *Repulse* and largest of all — HMS *Vanguard.*

The tonnage under construction in 1963 was both large and varied. Afloat in the outfit basin lay three vessels — HMS *Hampshire*, a guided-missile destroyer nearing completion, together with two — 20,000 ton gross Cunarders — the *Carmania* and *Franconia*, undergoing extensive conversions.

On the berths in the East Yard were HMS *Aurora* — a Leander class frigate and the assault ship HMS *Intrepid* together with TSMV *Centaur* — a cargo/passenger vessel for the Blue Funnel Line. On the berths in the West Yard was a 75,000 ton deadweight oil tanker for B.P. But only one vessel, a further tanker for B.P. was yet to commence. This work, although outfit intensive, did not constitute a particularly large order book consistent with the yard's size.

This then was the workload at the shipyard when I joined it. Prior to joining, I was invited to meet the other directors on a Saturday morning in the "model room". This lovely room was so-called because around its walls were hung "half models" of ships built in the yard, while around the perimeter of the room stood six finished models of ships in glass cases. In the centre of the room stood a huge mahogany table surrounded by chairs. I was courteously received but remember thinking afterwards how formal it was compared to Lithgows.

On my first morning, John Rannie had assembled all the managers and head foremen in what was to be my office. Each one of them carried a bowler hat. They must have wondered how it came to be that this young man from the Lower Clyde was now to be their chief. I certainly felt this acutely. After introductions, I was taken on board *Carmania* and *Franconia,* which were being converted from pure passenger ships into cruise ships. I was immediately impressed with the scale of everything — large ships, men everywhere — and very complicated!

I found everything very strange at first — the sheer numbers of managers for instance made it certain that delegation was the order of the day. There could be no "yard manager and his two assistants" here. Gradually I settled in and began to see the picture more clearly. I thought the steel working facilities were very poor in the East Yard. The berth cranage was all fixed and of fairly light safe working load. The West Yard steel facilities had been recently upgraded and were much better in all respects. The latest plate cutting machines, large prefabrication shed and heavy travelling berth cranes were all evidence of this.

I could come to no conclusion about the condition of the outfit shops, since I had no experience of anything like this. All I saw were enormous shops, jammed full of equipment. The largest — the joiners shop, could and did support a joinery workforce of some 1,200 men. I did not like what I saw of the rate of production. It seemed to me that despite the size and complexity of the ships, there were far too many men and lots of them doing very little!

To my surprise, the management team which I inherited were immediately supportive. I had imagined that one or more of them might have seen himself more fitted than I for the job. It was quickly apparent however, that they expected to be led and would carry out instructions immediately. The head foreman, who wielded considerable power, felt likewise.

The one word that more than any other described Brown's was "tradition". It was to be one of several reasons for its downfall. John Rannie's predecessor as Shipyard Director was Donald Skiffington (later Sir Donald). He directed shipyard affairs for 25 years and presided over many of the famous ships mentioned earlier. He did this in a highly autocratic manner, which worked very well in the 20's and 30's but would have cut little ice in the 60's.

John Rannie reigned over the yard for close on 20 years and like Sir Donald, led from the front. He could be very flambuoyant and expansive, particularly when dealing with the Press. He was an immensely honest and likeable big man. In the yard I found that he could be very hard on the management, but not quite so hard on the labourforce. He was certainly a personality with a capital 'P' — and the management loved it! He was known as J.R. — and South Fork had not even been invented!

But a few months in a new job is far too soon to be forming judgments of the work place and in any case, I soon became too busy to sit down and think about such things. The Shipyard Director was not only responsible for production but also for labour relations. This latter subject came to absorb large chunks of each working day. Whereas in most yards the boilermaker trades were most likely to be the first to claim increases in pay and conditions with the outfit trades following, in Brown's it was frequently the opposite. The convenor of the shipyard shop stewards was a plumber and the vice-convenor an electrician. Both were very left-wing. They were highly articulate and soft spoken, but what they said was usually "dynamite". They developed many claims for increased wages and conditions over the years.

The outfit work on passenger liners requires quite large numbers of tradesmen, some in the shops but predominantly on the ships. As a particular liner approached the launch stage, more and more outfit trades would be recruited. This was a source of industrial relations trouble. Some communist elements were able to infiltrate the yard, despite the staff being fully aware of the individuals concerned. One could then expect many and various claims, overtime bans and stoppages.

A passenger liner represents a major investment by the shipowner concerned who naturally wishes the new ship to be an immediate commercial success. He thus requires to advertise the vessel's maiden voyage many months in advance of delivery in order to ensure maximum bookings. If the delivery date is not maintained, not only will the bookings have to be cancelled with all the adverse publicity that this involves, but just as bad for the shipowner, he has paid most of the instalments of the price due to the builder for as yet no return. Hence the delivery of a liner is of crucial importance and imposes immense pressures upon the builder. The shop stewards were fully aware of this and exploited this position to the full in order to extract higher wages.

I was still a member of the Conference and Claims Committee of the Clyde Shipbuilders Association, but now of course representing Brown's. Outfit trade disputes arose in the yard and while the pressures described above were continuous, the other members of the Committee had their own yards to think about. They had no intention of allowing me to concede increases at Brown's which could be passed on to every yard on the Clyde. In many instances, there was little if any justification for the claims from our workforce. I frequently felt inclined to fight them to the finish and indeed on a number of occasions we suffered major strikes. But in the end, with or without a strike, they quite often achieved an increase. It was "damage limitation".

Another problem adversely affecting production was the late issue of drawings from the ship drawing office. While well used to complex vessels, especially passenger vessels, they seemed indifferent to the requirements of the production department to meet deadlines. There was an ingrained tradition that the owner must be satisfied. The fact that frequently this involved both time and money made no difference. An example will illustrate this.

It is normal in the case of a passenger liner, for the builders to contract to construct a number of full-size "sample cabins". It is also normal for the owner to employ "decorative architects" to design both the public rooms and passenger cabins. Although no doubt highly qualified and frequently famous for some previous decorative work for which they had been responsible, some of them, like the drawing office, had little if any idea of either time or money. The drawing office and the joinery department, both weaned on a diet of "cost plus" contracts, bent over backwards to develop the themes of the architects. Time passed while the owner and architects continued to modify the designs. Eventually all was agreed and at long last the joiner shop could begin manufacture to a design that had not been allowed for in the original price.

But of course, the work did not always consist of passenger ships, with the problems that such vessels posed for industrial relations. In 1963, the yard landed an order for a number of jack-up drilling rigs from the Offshore Company, Houston, Texas. The arrival of the Texans in the shipyard was like a breath of fresh air. They were delightful people and spoke with the slow drawl of the South, in between puffs of long green cigars. A few of them wore ten gallon hats and all of them wore winkle-toed boots.

A jack-up rig is designed with long heavy legs which pass vertically through jackhouses located at each corner of the hull. On station for drilling, the legs are jacked down by pumps until they reach the sea bed. Further pumping implants the legs firmly on to the rock. Still further pumping cannot move the legs downward and so the hull rises up the legs. The rig can then continue drilling in bad weather with the hull well clear of heavy seas.

The legs on our rigs were 364 feet in height and most of these were fitted in sections with the rig moored in the Gareloch, in the Lower Clyde. The Admiralty charts indicated a hole in the sea bed at a particular point, deep enough to permit the legs being fully lowered. When all sections had been fitted and welded, the system required to be tested by lifting the hull clear of the water with the legs implanted on the sea bed. The test was finally abandoned after we had lowered the legs no less than 90 feet below the so-called sea bed. There was no rock — only mud! (*See illustration*).

One of the naval vessels building around this time was HMS *Intrepid*, the second of two assault ships. The first, HMS *Fearless* was built by Harland & Wolff in Belfast, who were responsible for the issue of drawings for both ships. Unfortunately the drawings were not forthcoming at a time when the yard was very short of steelwork. Pressure was immediately put on the Belfast builders by both naval staff and our own yard, in order to try and expedite progress. Naval staff were of course kept fully informed of the the resulting delay to the ship.

At this time, the yard landed a major order — that of *Kungsholm*, a cruise liner for the Swedish American Line. In addition, further orders were obtained for drilling rigs and also for a handy size bulk carrier.

Intrepid was launched in June 1964, (*See illustration*) but outfitting could not proceed because of the persistent lack of information. The ship was delayed 6 months. The Navy had hoped that it could be available for British Troops landing on Aden, but this was not possible. The Navy was warned that we now had a very heavy programme of work and that we fully intended to honour our commitments in respect of this work. Further failure to produce the drawings would result in all these new vessels "leap frogging" delivery of *Intrepid*. In the end, this is exactly what happened — the ship even missed the evacuation from Aden! But not before an amusing incident occurred.

By the time the drawings eventually arrived, much of our labour was committed elsewhere although we still employed some on *Intrepid*. The Navy were now of course pressing hard for delivery and demanded daily figures of labour employed on board. They did not believe the figures they received and so posted a sailor on one of the ship's gangways to physically count our men as they went on

Jack-up drilling rig *Orion* completed 30th June 1966.

My first speaking engagement! Acceptance of drilling rig *Orion*, 21st June 1966 (my wife in the centre).

Launch of the assault ship HMS *Intrepid*, 25th June 1964.

board. He failed to count our men coming down the other two gangways and onto our other ships!

The traditions pervading the Company ran very deep and in *Kungsholm*, I was able to see a liner built from the beginning in the yard's traditional manner. The hull outfitting of a liner is the heart of the job and it is imperative to finish off steelwork in the lower decks as soon as possible, so as to permit outfit trades to commence in these areas. The aim is to have a number of lower deck cabins completed and locked up by the launch date.

In the case of Brown's, the first of the outfit trades to arrive on board was the joiners, who after lining-off immediately began erecting the wood bulkheads which form the cabins. As more and more areas of steelwork were released for outfit, so more and more joiners were recruited and more and more cabins were formed. Now it's relatively simple and fast to undertake this work. What is neither simple nor fast is the work of the plumber, who has to install a variety of different pipe systems — fire and washdeck, sewage, scuppers, hot and cold fresh water etc. Some of these pipes measured up to 5 inches or more in diameter and were full of bends, tee-pieces and joints and where they passed through decks, required welding in place. The electrician and the sheetiron worker responsible for the ventilation trunking had a slightly easier task.

Inboard of the cabins on either side of a ship runs an alleyway, the ceiling of which is used to support the main runs of piping, cabling and trunking. All three trades were struggling to install their products, hemmed in now by the cabin bulkheads. I began to seriously question whether the joiners should not be the last of the outfit trades to commence work on board. But the show was on the road and it would have made things even worse I believe, to change the system at that point in time.

But this traditional method had a number of far-reaching consequences. When a plumber was "sketching" a pipe on board, later to be bent in accordance with the sketch, he found the run of pipe obstructed by these cabin bulkheads. So instead of the pipe being manufactured in say, one length of 15 feet, three shorter lengths had to be manufactured. Not only did this add to the shopwork, but far more crucially, it created much additional shipwork. Moreover when the plumber came to install the piping, considerable damage was suffered by the woodwork. Finally, the provision of all these cabin areas, many of them not yet inhabited by other outfit trades, were fine places in which to loaf?

The management however, considered that this was the way to outfit a liner and anyway, hadn't they produced some of the World's finest? There was a momentum about the whole thing that could not be halted. The same precisely occurred later on the *QE2*.

The workmanship I have not yet mentioned. It was of a uniformly high standard in all trades and the *Kungsholm's* joiner work in particular was quite magnificent.

The owner's inspectors were very exacting. For example, two of them were allotted the task of inspecting the passenger cabins. Armed with powerful torches, notebooks and pencils, they examined every square inch of each cabin. One of them stepped inside the commodious wardrobe and closed the door. Emerging some minutes later, he would then make copious notes — just about the wardrobe! Copies of the notes for blocks of cabins were then passed to our manager in charge of this section of the ship. These were the defect lists. Until each tiny defect was corrected and some of them were arguably not defects, the subject cabin was deemed unacceptable by the owners.

The ship herself was delivered in April 1966 and was a commercial disaster. (*See illustration*) The scale of this disaster was spelled out at a Clydebank board meeting some months after delivery.

Board meetings were held quarterly and were very formal affairs presided over by Lord Aberconway. By tradition, the shipyard director was placed at the bottom of the table, opposite the Chairman. The three non-executive directors faithfully attended every meeting. Sir Eric Mensforth, Chairman of Westland and a master cutler, was a diminutive and highly intelligent man, much given to asking probing questions. He sat halfway down one side of the table. Directly opposite sat Lord Bilsland, a Glasgow industrialist whose fortune was founded in bakeries. He was also rather small with silvery hair and he must have been well into his seventies. In front of his Lordship was placed an enormous solid silver cigarette box, in the centre compartment of which were laid out Abdullah No. 3 cigarettes, much favoured by him. He smoked two of these at each meeting.

Next to me on my right was placed Mr. R. J. Barclay, a retiring

TSMV *Kingsholm*, completed 11th March 1966.

bachelor who curiously enough, lived in a pub high in the Peak District. No sooner had the Chairman opened the proceedings than R. J. Barclay would slowly open his jacket to reveal an inside pocket lined with pens and bulging with papers. For the next two hours he would systematically read each paper following which he would quietly tear each one into the smallest pieces. By lunchtime two ashtrays were overflowing with neatly torn paper. He seldom asked a question. Lord Bilsland never spoke, but from time to time, a nod of the head accompanied by a purring noise indicated his approval of the Chairman's remarks. All three non-executive directors were extremely courteous and supportive.

At a previous board meeting the Chairman had enquired of the Secretary, the financial outcome of Ship No. 728 — *Kungsholm*. He was informed that not all material suppliers final bills had come to hand. He assured the Chairman that the final cost would be available at the next board meeting. This was duly minuted.

At the next Board Meeting the secretary spelled out the extent of the contract loss. It was very serious. The Chairman remained silent, turned to gaze out of the window for what seemed an age, turned back to face the Board and uttered only two words — " How tiresome!"

It was also traditional for the John Brown & Co. Ltd., main board members to host a dinner for the directors of each subsidiary once a year. The first of these that I attended was held in a private room at the Dorchester. The seating plan indicated that main board directors were placed between subsidiary directors around the oval table. I was placed between Lord Clitheroe, whom I had not previously met and Lord Bilsland. I had just filled my first spoonful of consommé when Lord Clitheroe turned to me and enquired in a loud voice — "I say Parker, what do you think of the situation in Angola?" Incidentally, the year was 1963, long before a war had broken out in that country. My problem was not so much the situation in Angola, but where was the bloody place!

The outfitting of *Kungsholm* had been an exhausting business. Frequently I toured the ship late at night, encouraging the night shift and assessing progress and identifying bottlenecks. I suggested to John Rannie that I take two weeks holiday abroad with my wife, but combine this with visiting a number of European Shipyards. He had a word with the Chairman who at the conclusion of the next board meeting, drew me aside and said — "The board want you to take a holiday with your wife for which the Company will bear the cost. I understand you wish to visit some shipyards. This sounds to me like a busman's holiday — just see that you don't spend too long in the driver's cab!" So the schedule was arranged — a shipyard visit in the morning, rejoining my wife for lunch and thereafter sightseeing.

We flew first to Amsterdam and from there I visited the yards of Wilton-Fizenoord and Van Der Giessen. I knew a Dutch manager at Wilton's whom my father had trained at the Caledon yard and who had taken the wise precaution of marrying a Dundee girl. We saw a little of this pleasant couple during our short stay in Amsterdam. Then it was on to Hamburg, there to see the Deutsche-Werft and Howaldtswerke yards. Naturally one of the sightseeing trips was round the Hamburg docks — still very much in the "driver's cab". I was delighted to note shipyard personnel idling away their time on ships fitting out. It quite reminded me of home!

We next flew to Copenhagen and there I visited Burmeister and Wain's yard. In the northern outskirts of the city is located the factory of H. Nielson A/S — manufacturers of shipyard cranes and plate handling devices. The export director was well known to me, one Val Gröenholm by name. He was an indefatigable and hugely successful salesman, who had won orders in far-flung corners of the World. He spoke excellent English and spoke it very fast. He was a first class host and immediately took us in hand.

One evening he escorted us to a restaurant in the centre of the city called, "The Seven Nations" — alas now closed — where each of the seven interconnected small dining rooms was furnished in the style of a different country. He led us on a tour of the premises, while startled diners were cut short in their conversations as Val stretched across their table to point out some picture or carving adorning the walls.

We were seated in the Japanese Room and Val requested permission to order the meal on our behalf. My wife let it slip that it was her birthday whereupon Val quickly recalled the waiter and spoke to him quietly in Danish. The meal was quite delicious. Gravadlax with schnapps and beer, followed by reindeer meat, redcurrant jelly, accompanied by a good wine and then the sweet.

The sweet arrived on a large silver salver carried high by the waiter. On it reposed a three-funnelled edible ship! At one end of the tray stood a small silver pole from the top of which a blinding magnesium flare suddenly illuminated our section of the restaurant. The flare went out and a Union Jack hung limply from the pole. Clever these Japanese!

The meal eaten, Val then suggested we leave "The Seven Nations" and walk the few hundred yards to the sister restaurant — "The Seven Sma Hames" — where we would have coffee and brandy. Again we toured the restaurant before sampling the Armagnac.

From Copenhagen we took the Hydrofoil to Malmö in Sweden. There I was able to see the advanced state of shipbuilding technology achieved by Kockum's yard. We travelled by rail to Gothenburg, where three shipyards were visited, that of Eriksberg, Lindholmen and the new Arendal shipyard of Götaverken.

We then flew on to Oslo, where I visited Nylands yard, which was the least impressive of those visited. From Oslo we flew to Bergen in a piston-engined plane called a "Metropolitan". Although there was no sign of snow in the city, it was still lying deep on the Norwegian mountains over which we had to fly to reach Bergen. The little plane was full and it appeared to be labouring hard to gain height to clear the mountain range — in fact we always seemed to be the same height from the ground. Bergen was safely reached where we joined the boat for Newcastle-upon-Tyne. The whole trip had taken a little over two weeks and did us both a power of good.

Prior to delivery of *Kungsholm*, the Company obtained the contract to build the *QE2*. Bells were rung in Clydebank churches, signifying the joy felt locally, particularly in relation to employment prospects. The ship was contracted for delivery in November 1968. At the outset, the Chairman and other non-executive directors were alarmed at the prospect of this huge contract sustaining losses on a scale much larger than *Kungsholm*. They had been made aware of two of the yard's difficulties. First, while one can tell at a glance when say half of the labour cost allowed in the estimate has been spent, it is extremely difficult to estimate whether one has completed half of the work. Second, that it is equally difficult to keep track of all alterations and deviations from the original specification, since they could occur in the technical department or at any one of the shipyard production departments.

In an effort to overcome these problems, they proposed that we make use of a firm of chartered surveyors known to them, who had been rated a big success with Constructor John Brown Ltd. The idea was that the surveyors would be installed in Clydebank for the duration of the contract and would try to record every alteration and deviation from the contract and at the same time, try to assess the percentage of work done by each trade at any given point in time. Both were huge tasks. Success in the first one was wholly dependant upon the staff throughout the yard advising the surveyors of alterations. Provided they did so, the surveyors were confident of their ability to develop large substantiated claims against the owners, both for time and money. I personally doubted whether they could achieve the second objective, since they would first have to be taught shipbuilding! But I was happy to co-operate because even if they only scored with the first aim, it would be well worth their fee. They were duly installed in the yard and work commenced.

Both Cunard and Brown's wanted a formal keel laying ceremony. As I have already mentioned, the berth cranes in the East Yard were of light safe working load. It was not considered good publicity to restrict the weight of the first prefabricated unit to the modest capability of this craneage. Two cranes in tandem could not be used, because the cranes were fixed and out of reach of each other. So it was decided to construct a prefabricted unit of double the weight that could be lifted and merely slide it into position, using a fixed berth crane with its lifting wire led through a series of snatch blocks connected to the concreted berth and thence to the unit itself.

At the appointed time and with all the owners and builders officials and the Press in attendance, the order was given to "take the strain". No-one could detect the slightest movement of the unit. More strain was applied and very slowly concrete blocks began to come out of the ground! At least the Press liked it!

The huge vessel gradually took shape and large areas of steelwork were completed in good time for release to the outfit trades. Visitors from far and wide came to view this third "Queen" superliner, including a large deputation of M.P.'s led by the Prime Minister, then Mr. Harold Wilson. (*See illustration*).

There was speculation about the name the ship was to bear and

Lecturing Manny Shinwell during visit to *QE2* by Harold Wilson and a large deputation of MPs, summer 1967.

this speculation grew as the ship approached its launch. Her Majesty the Queen had graciously consented to perform the launch ceremony and so the date had been fixed the previous year. The date selected was the 20th September 1967. Since the ship had no name, the launch invitations bore the yard number of the ship — No. 736.

Preparations for this huge Royal event started many months previously and reached a crescendo on the eve of the launch.

CHAPTER 10

THE LAUNCH OF THE *QE2*

ONE tradition at Brown's which I thoroughly approved of was the launch procedure. Over the years, the yard had been honoured by hosting a number of Royal ships sponsors and so the procedure for Royal launches became the procedure for all launches. When the time came for the Queen to launch *QE2*, I felt at home with the system, if not the actuality.

The procedure commenced some days before the launch when I inspected and tested the launch triggers (which release the ship), the drag chains (which immediately check the ship as soon as she is afloat) and their connections to the hull, the ramming gear (pumps which can push the end of the launchways) and the general condition of the berth to ensure that it was free of obstructions to the drag chains.

A small wooden box fixed to the top of the port side launchway contained a number of electric lightbulbs. When the sponsor released the triggers, they would on falling, complete an electric circuit and the bulbs would light up. There was one bulb for each trigger. By this means the shipyard director could have visual confirmation that all triggers had dropped. For cargo liners and small tankers for instance, three triggers were fitted to each side of the ship. In the case of *QE2*, there were ten triggers (and ten lightbulbs) in total. Prior to the 20th September 1967 I tested this equipment on three separate occasions with 100% success.

Meanwhile preparations for hosting the event were in their final stages. John Rannie took personal charge of these and it was truly a masterly performance. In the event, there were no less than five large launch stands for invited guests, the principal one being at the bow of the ship and the other four in line down the port side. Including all yard employees and their wives and friends, invited guests and World Press, no less than 32,000 people watched the spectacle at close quarters. The Press alone numbered five hundred! A pipe band was in attendance at each side of the vessel — playing different tunes! But for me, the way in which the Queen was able to see everyone and everyone to see her, was a touch of genius. A raised platform, no more than two feet above the ground was laid out along her path through the shipyard and down to the bow of the ship. Simple and highly effective.

Late on the evening of the 19th September, with everything ready and checked, I felt a compelling desire to go to the shipyard. It was a calm moonlit night as I walked down under the silent ship. To my surprise, I met the head foreman shipwright. It was his 47th launch and again tradition, he had bought his 47th bowler hat. I said what was on my mind — "I realise that we've tested the triggers successfully on three separate occasions, but supposing just supposing, one of them fails to drop?" He replied — "There's no need to worry — at each trigger I've positioned the biggest shipwrights on Clydeside, each one armed with a sledgehammer. If a trigger doesn't fall, it will be smashed to the ground in seconds!" I drove home somewhat relieved.

On launch day, the guests were assembled, the bands were playing and the giant ship lay ready for launching, except for the last remaining keel and bilge blocks which were being knocked out. Above the sound of the hammering and the pipe bands, I heard cheering. The launch party was on its way. After being presented to the Queen, I led the Royal launch party down under the ship to explain the trigger mechanism, following which I returned them to the launch platform. (*See illustration*) I positioned myself opposite the box containing the light bulbs and waited.

The Queen named the ship, released the bottle and pressed the launch button. To my horror, only nine bulbs lit up — the second trigger on the starboard side had not dropped! The ship remained motionless. I was in the best possible position to detect any movement, as I was standing right up against the ship. On the platform, they were anxiously awaiting a signal from me that the ship had started to move.

Almost five minutes elapsed (it felt like five years), before the ship imperceptably began to move. I tore my hat off in relief and in the same

Inspecting the launch arrangements of *QE2* in the company of Her Majesty the Queen, 20th September 1967.

spirit, gave the ship a helping shove. The ship gathered speed and slid into the Clyde in truly majestic style, the bow dipping in a curtsey as she did so. (*See illustration*) Within minutes I learned what had happened. The offending trigger had not dropped because under the weight of the vessel, it had actually deformed. This was the reason why it took nearly five minutes to smash it to the ground.

The invited guests made their way to the brand-new workers canteen where champagne and cake was served. The Chairmen of the owners and builders jointly presented the Queen with a speedboat, which they revealed by drawing back curtains hanging behind the top table. This beautiful craft was gleaming in dark blue and white paint and had been specially constructed to fit the davits of the Royal Yacht *Britannia* (another Clydebank product).

After thanking the Chairmen for the elegant gift, the Queen remarked — "I think we will name this ship "Brown" and paint it in Cunard colours". In a loud aside, the Duke of Edinburgh said — "No, we'll call it "Cunard" and paint it brown!"

Some day, some launch!

I was mightily relieved!

CHAPTER 11

MERGER DISCUSSIONS

In the early 60's a number of shipyards on the Upper Clyde closed. Harland & Wolff at Govan, together with A. & J. Inglis at Pointhouse were first to go followed by the world famous Denny's of Dumbarton, Simon-Lobnitz at Renfrew and Blythswood at Scotstoun. The same pattern was being repeated on the Lower Clyde.

In 1965 the Fairfield Shipbuilding Co. Ltd,. together with its Engineering subsidiary, Fairfield-Rowan, went into receivership. This was one of Clydeside's largest yards with a proud record of building many famous liners and warships. The fear of large-scale unemployment loomed large. George Brown, a senior member of the Cabinet, spent some time on Clydeside attempting to save the company.

Eventually, a local industrialist, Sir Iain Stewart and two other local businessmen were persuaded to purchase the company assisted by Government finance and to a lesser extent by trade union finance. In February 1966, the shipyard continued ship-building under its new name — Fairfield (Glasgow) Ltd. The "Fairfield Experiment" as it came to be known, was determined to prove that work study, production control, value analysis and other planning techniques could be successfully applied to shipbuilding.

On the 16th February 1965, the Government had appointed a committee, known as the Shipbuilding Enquiry Committee, "To establish what changes are necessary in organisation, in the methods of production and any other factors affecting costs, to make the shipbuilding industry competitive in World markets; to establish what changes in organisation and methods of production would reduce the costs of manufacture of large main engines of ships to the lowest level; and to recommend what action should be taken by employers, trade unions and Government, to bring about these changes".

The Chairman of the Committee was Mr. R. M. Geddes and on 24th February 1966, the findings and recommendations of the Geddes Report were made public. These were:—

1. The establishment of a Shipbuilding Industry Board (S.I.B.) which would, among other things, administer and control Government financial assistance.

2. The availability of Government loans, "Aimed at facilitating desirable groupings and accelerating the rationalisation of resources".

3. The availability of grants for transitional losses.

Both 2 and 3 above were subject to a number of criteria.

The Government duly set up the S.I.B. under the Chairmanship of Sir William Swallow. The Vice-Chairman of the S.I.B. was Anthony Hepper, while the remaining member of the board was Joe Gormley, President of the National Union of Mineworkers. They toured all U.K. shipyards and engineworks and discussed the possibilities of merging them into larger units.

During 1967, we at Clydebank learned of covert discussions taking place between Conneils, Stephens and Yarrows, to apparently investigate the feasibility of a merger. Fairfield (Glasgow) Ltd. and Brown's opened discussions for the same reason.

In our case, a technical and production committee was set up to explore the possibilities. The production committee met only twice and on the second occasion it became quite clear that our "cultures" were too far apart to permit of finding common ground on which to progress. The merger talks with Fairfield were accordingly abandoned and so too were the discussions among the other three yards. Later in 1967 I was informed that the five yards remaining on the Upper Clyde had agreed terms with the S.I.B. under which they could merge to form Upper Clyde Shipbuilders Ltd. (U.C.S.). The Chairman designate was named as Anthony Hepper.

Great concern was felt in Brown's about the future of shipbuilding on the Upper Clyde for a number of reasons. First, it was recognised that there was little in common between the five companies and it was difficult to see what benefits would accrue by merging, apart possibly from the benefits of bulk buying. Fairfield for example, continued to publicly denounce the methods employed by other U.K. shipbuilders and were creating a manufacturing facility dedicated to work study. Yarrows were wholly dedicated to Naval work, which work dictated a production facility, supervision and quality control dissimilar to the other four yards. Connells had traditionally built merchant ships of medium size and operated in the fashion of Lithgows Ltd. — minimum overheads, "no nonsense shipbuilding". Stephens built ships as large as Connells and as noted earlier, had a tradition of Naval building but in 1967 had a poor order book. Finally we recognised that Brown's would be basically unattractive to the other four, because our financial fortunes depended almost entirely on the commercial outcome of *QE2*, since we had little other work.

Second, we were worried in case the "Fairfield Experiment" rubbed off on us — high wages, huge planning staff and as yet, no tangible benefits. We believed the other three yards had similar misgivings in relation to Fairfields.

Third, we were concerned about the constitution of the U.C.S. board. Would it be controlled by shipbuilders?

Fourth, would all five yards be kept in being, or would one or more be closed under a rationalisation scheme?

Fifth, the disparity of wage rates across the five yards could give rise to claims for increases in both wages and conditions.

In the event many of our fears were justified. The date set for vesting was 7th February 1968.

CHAPTER 12

UPPER CLYDE SHIPBUILDERS

I spent a little over 18 months with U.C.S. and for the first time in my working life, did not look forward to Monday mornings.

Within three months of vesting, the U.C.S. board was in place. Two of the executive directors, that of technical and finance, were drawn from Clydebank. None of the remaining three had any experience of shipbuilding and their choice was presumably to give effect to the Chairman's belief that new blood and new ideas were required. The production director had been works director of a diesel engine manufacturer. The marketing director came from a well-known manufacturer of porcelain china. The industrial relations director had been employed, I believe, in a company manufacturing copper tubing.

The board, including the non-executive directors, presided over five Divisional Directors, one for each yard or division, as each was now described. I was appointed Divisional Director of the Clydebank division. The *QE2* was dubbed a special project and John Rannie was appointed Special Director in charge of *QE2*.

Since the *QE2* represented a large proportion of Clydebank's work-in-progress and absorbed some 80% or more of our work-force, I felt disappointed initially with this arrangement. Effectively it meant that although I was nominally responsible for the running of the yard, I had no responsibility for 80% of its labour force working physically on the premises. Henceforth of course, I took no further interest in the *QE2* and was to feel much relieved about that fact by the end of the year.

U.C.S. headquarters was located at Fitzpatrick House — it became known as "The Kremlin" — a modern office block not far from Glasgow's Central Station. The offices, carpeted throughout in specially woven material bearing the U.C.S. Maltese Cross emblem, soon began to be occupied by a bewildering variety of staff reporting direct to board members. This staff was all in addition to the existing staffs at each yard and represented a substantial additional overhead burden for the company. The Divisional Directors were all placed on one year contracts and at the same time given a substantial increase in salary. High grade cars were provided.

One of the first moves made by the production director was to hire a firm of management consultants already known to him, to investigate and report on the extent of production control and associated systems operational at each yard. Other consultants were engaged for a variety of different briefs. At one point, no less than five separate management consultants were at work in Clydebank.

Meanwhile, the unions had quickly sized up the new situation, which was "ripe for plucking". The payment systems were different at each yard and there were wide variations in "take home" pay between the same trade, especially boilermakers. Soon claims were pouring in. The outfitting of *QE2* was of course proving fertile ground for claims from the outfit trades in particular. Many of the claims were conceded by the new industrial relations department and the pace of work noticeably slowed down.

New orders were hard to come by and from where I sat in Clydebank, it seemed to me that if we were going to reflect the real cost of building ships in U.C.S. with its higher overheads and higher wages, we would be fortunate to land any. The marketing director appointed three people reporting directly to him. He decided apparently to slice the World into three portions and gave each of his assistants a slice in which to market for newbuildings. A few orders were taken however. It was as well since Clydebank had only a 37,000 ton deadweight bulk carrier on the stocks and a drilling rig outfitting, apart from the *QE2*. We badly needed work for steel trades. We received an order for a package lumber carrier on which we were able to start work as soon as the steel was delivered. Later in 1968, we received another order, this time from Fred Olsen, for a twin-screw ferry.

I saw a good deal of the board, but only very rarely at Clydebank. Many meetings were held at The Kremlin, mainly on industrial relation matters and productivity schemes. Very elaborate meetings of a whole day's duration were convened in the Central Station Hotel to discuss with the Confederation of Shipbuilding and Engineering unions the U.C.S new pay and productivity policy and the proposed new negotiating procedure.

But as Sir James Lithgow had remarked way back in 1947 — "We were told that higher wages would induce greater effort. This has not happened . . . . . One of the earliest lessons my father gave me some 45 years ago was, that when wages went up, output went down". The programme of ship deliveries was seriously slipping as wages rose and productivity fell.

The Divisions were each held to account. It seemed not to matter that the high wage rates and falling productivity had been the direct result of U.C.S. main board policies. The loans and grants to U.C.S. administered by the S.I.B. were likely to be exceeded by the company's trading losses and so it was decreed that suppliers payments should be delayed. This became imperative as instalments due from shipowners were delayed because of the programme slippage. It was reported that the *QE2*'s delivery date was seriously in jeopardy. This was at first denied by its management. The contract delivery date of end November 1968 was believed by them to be still feasible.

More and more I was beginning to feel an outsider and swimming against the tide. It seemed that because I had been trained in shipbuilding, my views and those of a similar training and experience, were suspect. I found myself disagreeing fundamentally with the new philosophies.

The *QE2* delivery meanwhile was, with the agreement of Cunard, delayed by a month. But the fall in productivity over a period of months had a serious effect on progress. Under the terms of the ship's contract, the builders were required to undertake technical trials in a tropical climate to prove the ship's air-conditioning system, while at the same time testing all other ship systems. Unfortunately, the accommodation areas were far from complete at the time of these trials and it became clear that the vessel could not now be completed until some time in 1969. A public row erupted and the situation was not helped by a problem which developed with the ship's turbines.

Turbines apart, I was not remotely surprised at the events which climaxed on board the vessel steaming off Las Palmas. As noted earlier, the outfit work had proceeded along "traditional lines", with the horrific results on a very much larger scale than *Kungsholm*. I set foot on *QE2* only once after U.C.S. had been formed. The ship was then in the Firth of Clyde drydock in Greenock and the time was some time in November. I didn't stay long. I was appalled at the vast amount of unfinished work.

I was doubly relieved to have been removed from *QE2* on February 5th 1968. First, because I profoundly disagreed with the outfit methods employed — that is, if they could be so described. Second, because of the effect of U.C.S. industrial relations policies on the delivery of this prestigious ship.

All that befell *QE2* was symptomatic of what was happening throughout U.C.S. The deterioration referred to continued, but with an added complication. The suppliers, whose payments had been postponed, began to take joint action by withholding supplies. By the Spring of 1969, I was encountering numerous examples of this. Delivery of the lumber carrier for instance, was placed in jeopardy because of the refusal of suppliers to release to us the anchors and lifeboats. Owners were publicly condemning our performance as shipbuilders and most if not all of our ships, had been delayed in delivery.

It may seem superfluous to mention, but under private owner-ship, although shipbuilding had always been a serious business, it had always been for me, an enjoyable experience. At whatever level of management, one always knew with certainty, that short of "putting one's hand in the till", or gross inefficiency, one had the full backing of one's superiors. This feeling of security and respect for one's superiors was I'm afraid, sadly lacking at U.C.S. There was an air of unreality about the whole business. It gradually became clear to me that an almighty crash was imminent.

By the summer of 1969, our ships were seriously delayed and the reasons for the delays reported to the board. The reasons were neither accepted or rejected — there was no reaction. Finally at a meeting with the Chairman in early September 1969, I resigned from U.C.S. It was clear six months earlier that the policies being pursued would cause the demise of the Consortium. In the event, the company lurched from crisis to crisis, board members resigned one by one and in June 1971 the Consortium went into receivership.

With hindsight, I am fairly sure that without the umbrella of Loans and Grants made available to U.C.S. by the S.I.B., Brown's could not have survived. In all probability, neither would Connells or Stephens. What however is certain, is that U.C.S. speeded up the process of shipbuildings disintegration on the Upper Clyde. Only Yarrows and Fairfield survived.

CHAPTER 13

SWAN HUNTER SHIPBUILDERS LTD.

I was now aged 40 and for a short time seriously thought of trying to change my career. I soon realised however, that although mergers and take-overs were taking place across the U.K. shipbuilding industry, in none of them, with the exception of U.C.S., was the resulting business managed by other than professional shipbuilders. I determined to stay in the industry. And so like many a Scot before me, I kicked a stone or two out of Hadrians Wall, arrived on Tyneside and joined Swan Hunter Shipbuilders Ltd. The U.C.S merger was as nothing in scale compared to what had recently transformed the shape of the shipbuilding industry on the North East coast.

Traditionally, five separate shipbuilding companies had operated on Tyneside. The largest of these was Swan Hunter and Wigham Richardson Ltd., who operated a large yard at Wallsend, a medium-sized yard called "Neptune", the two connected by their shiprepairing facility equipped with four graving docks.

The company also owned two marine engineworks, a foundry and a construction company, all on Tyneside. In the space of a year or so, prior to my joining the company, they had taken over no less than three shipyards on the Tyne, two shipyards on the Tees, a small shipyard on the Tyne and at Goole in Yorkshire and with it substantial repair interests in one of the companies taken over. Swan Hunter Group Ltd. as they became known, then employed some 14,000 people and were the sole shipbuilders on the Rivers Tyne and Tees.

The companies were then regrouped into subsidiaries. By far the largest of these was Swan Hunter Shipbuilders Ltd., which consisted of six shipyards — Wallsend and Neptune yards, Vickers Naval yard, Hawthorn Leslie, John Redheads and the Haverton Hill yard on Teesside.

Smiths Dock Co. Ltd., also on Teesside, was run separately because of its higher wage rates but its extensive shiprepair facilities were split. The smaller portion that existed alongside the yard, remained under the control of Smiths Dock. The larger portion that was located at North Shields, was merged with Swan Hunter's Wallsend Dry Docks to form Swan Hunter Shiprepairers Ltd. The Goole Shipyard was merged with Clelands of Tyneside to form Swan Hunter Small Ship Division. The engineworks, foundry and construction company were left to operate independently.

This huge shipbuilding complex was full of work, especially at the Wallsend and Neptune yards, where I was appointed in charge of production. Wallsend was building a series of massive 253,000 tons deadweight oil tankers. Neptune was building two guided-missile destroyers and four fast cargo liners for the British India Steam Navigation Co. Ltd. (*See illustration*). I discovered to my immense relief that here again was shipbuilding as I knew it. There wasn't a consultant or a porcelain chinaman in sight! The management was friendly and co-operative and the activity in both yards was intense. It had to be, especially at Wallsend.

These huge tankers were built in a conventional manner, but were too long to fit into the largest berth. They were built at an angle, straddling two adjacent berths. When fully built, the great bulbous bow towered over Wallsend (the end of Hadrians Wall was actually in the yard), while the forecastle deck towered over the houses at the top of the bank adjacent to the yard fence. The stern jutted well out into the river. A vee-section of land had to be excavated from the opposite riverbank because the river was not quite wide enough at this point for launching purposes. After launching, it looked as though the River Tyne had acquired a new bridge!

The shipbuilding programme called for each tanker to be on the building berth for a little under twelve months. This may seem a long time, but the amount of steelwork involved required a yard average throughput of around 750 tons of steel per week. Some

A striking photograph of a British India Steam Navigation Company cargo liner
ready for launch at Swan Hunter's Neptune Yard.

weeks it was very much in excess of this. I personally didn't much like these ships. They were flat-bottomed, slab-sided, masses of steel, ugly in the extreme. The cargo oil tanks were giant caverns and measured 87 feet in depth, with a sheer a drop from deck to keel. For the four years I spent at Swan Hunter, I was involved with four of these giants. (*See illustration*).

Neptune yard had a varied programme of work, a mixture of naval and merchant. The contrast between the building of supertankers and naval vessels was very marked indeed. The thickness of the steel plating on a destroyer is paper-thin compared to the material used in supertankers, while the fine lines of the destroyers contrasted greatly with the bluff lines of supertankers. The construction programme of a destroyer spanned years not months, because of course the ship is jammed full of highly sophisticated electrical gear, weapon systems and computers.

Sometimes I became somewhat impatient with the established procedures and progress meetings that characterised the building of naval ships. Naval staff attach the utmost importance to cardinal date programmes, until that is, they decide to make some modification to the structure or the equipment. Frequently therefore, the shipbuilders efforts to maintain the building schedule laid down in the programme, could be destroyed at a stroke by a series of modifications. This caused me on one occasion to remark to the Principal Naval Overseer — "Now I realise why you paint all your ships grey. It's got little to do with camouflage. It's because nothing you say or do is ever black or white!"

Labour relations at Swan Hunter were in the main, a great deal better than I had experienced in Clydebank. The men worked appreciably harder and not surprisingly their wages were lower. The industrial relations department staff were mostly trained in shipbuilding. If a serious dispute broke out, Tom McIver, the Group Managing Director, took a hand in the proceedings.

Every shipyard boasts at least one comic and Wallsend was no exception. He was a welder and used to write topical verse in the quarterly works magazine. He called himself "Ripyard Cuddling!" The boilermakers were on strike at the time one of the editions of the magazine was issued. His latest poem made references to the dispute and ended with the lines—

"We don't want a pound and we don't want a fiver,
We just want parity with Tom McIver!"

One of the Swan Hunter super tankers leaving the river Tyne for trials, November 1971.

It wasn't only the management that I found friendly on Tyneside. Geordies in the main are a friendly lot, cheery with a good sense of humour and much addicted to Newcastle Broon Ale or Newcastle Exhibition or "Scotch" beer, depending on his taste. I had not heard of these "foreign" drinks when I was house-hunting at the end of 1969 in the northern outskirts of Newcastle. I ventured into a pub. The fellow in front of me was next to order — "A pint of Scotch please, hinney", he said. I couldn't believe it! Walking through Wallsend one afternoon, I saw a large crowd gathered near a church. I asked a passing workman if a wedding was in progress — "Why aye man, it's a big society affair — a welder's marrying a commoner".

Only a week or two after starting work with Swan Hunter, the company announced an order for a cruise liner for Norwegian Amerika Line. The ship was to be constructed in the Neptune shipyard.

Here we go again!

CHAPTER 14

VISTAFJORD

TWO things were made clear at the outset. First, that although the contract delivery date was end September 1973, the ship would be programmed for actual delivery on 17th May 1973, Norwegian Independence Day. Some eighteen years previously a smaller vessel — *Bergensfjord*, had been built for the same owners by Swan Hunter and delivered on Independence Day some four and a half months ahead of contract delivery date. Second, the planning department calmly announced that, so far as they were concerned, this cruise liner would be regarded as a special project. Accordingly, they would second personnel to me and henceforth these personnel would act independently of the planning department and report direct to me.

It was perfectly clear to me why the planning department took this line. Many of the passenger liners built in the U.K. since the end of the Second World War had been late in delivery, or suffered contract losses, or both. I am sure that the planning department believed that this ship would suffer a similar fate. They wanted no connection with this contract and this arrangement suited me to perfection.

While I was getting to grips with my new responsibilities early in 1970, I began to think very carefully about planning the construction of this liner. I kept bearing in mind the two major factors that had badly affected construction progress on such vessels at Clydebank. First, the failure of the drawing office to deliver drawings on time and second, the dire consequences of the joiners commencing their work on board too early in relation to other outfit trades.

In so far as the first factor was concerned, I was fortunate for two reasons. For a start, the drawing office was not hidebound by tradition and could bring fresh minds to bear on meeting the challenge posed by the building of a passenger ship. Second, the owners had taken delivery of the *Sagafjord* in 1965 from the Forges et Ch Mediterranee yard in France and the plans of that ship were made available to our drawing office. The new ship was generally similar to *Sagafjord*, but had an additional deck of superstructure. Thus a good deal of valuable information was available from the outset.

One of the features of the building programme of Clydebank-built passenger liners was the very early start made to the ship following contract signature. This was probably not of the yard's choosing so much as the need to start the vessel because of lack of other work. It may well have been another reason why the drawing office at that yard never seemed able to meet the requirements of production. But with *Vistafjord*, the contract was obtained in December 1969 and the ship was not contracted for delivery until September 1973 (but programmed as stated for 17th May 1973). The reason of course that the ship was contracted for on this date, was simply because of Swan Hunters bulging order book. But at least this ensured that the drawing office had a lot more time to develop the drawings.

Most of the public rooms on a passenger ship are located high up in the ship and so too are the cabin suites, where the most expensive fares can be charged. The lower down the ship the cabin, the lower the fare. If, for any reason, we ran late in delivery of the vessel, then at least I wanted to ensure that the unfinished cabins would be the "cheap" ones. This simple strategy dictated the outline building sequence. The order of build would therefore be to start on the lowest deck amidships and work upwards and gradually outwards simultaneously — pyramid fashion. This plan would allow work to commence on the public rooms and "expensive" cabins at the earliest possible time.

I did not relish repeating another feature of Clydebank's traditional methods, namely — to have outfit trades working all over the vessel at any given time. I wanted to concentrate the men into smaller areas, which could be better supervised. And of course I had no intention of allowing cabin bulkheads in one area to be erected until the piping, wiring and ventilation was nearing completion in that area.

With all this in mind, I asked our little planning team to subdivide the whole ship into sixty-four blocks and run a preliminary programme based on ten weeks outfitting time for each block of cabins. This programme was refined to allow a gradual build-up of outfit trades on board with a corresponding run-down at the latter end, but at no time manning more than twelve blocks simultaneously. I discussed this concept of build strategy with the drawing office and they were at once enthusiastic and co-operative, even although this meant far-reaching changes to their normal order of issuing drawings. The conventional method was to issue a general arrangement plan of an entire deck. But I wanted parts of different decks. The same changes had to be made to the order of drawing and issuing of steel plans, which of course precede the outfit ones. From these discussions, we were able to construct a master plan showing for each of sixty-four blocks, the start and finish date of a) drawings, b) steelwork and c) outfit. I proposed to monitor progress on a weekly basis with all concerned.

I briefed all departments on the new outfitting concept and explained the programme and weekly monitoring. All were happy with the arrangement except for the joinery manager. He was concerned that the initial exclusion of his department from an outfit block might not leave it sufficient time to complete it to programme. He was finally persuaded that the system would work, since by the time he did receive the "green light", he would have a clear run of the block in question. This discussion was extremely important for another reason. From it evolved the idea of joiner work prefabrication. The joinery manager was convinced that the wood bulkheads, shipside linings and furniture would be available from the joiners shop for each block at the normal time. What was his department supposed to do while awaiting completion of other outfit trades work?

The answer was to connect part of the shipside lining to the bedside console. The console consisted of a bedside locker, wired for radio, call buttons and telephone. The electricians could in fact complete the internal wiring of this unit before it was lifted on board. In the same way, wardrobes could be connected to part of the cabin bulkheads and it too pre-wired before being fitted on board.

Such prefabricated joinery units were too heavy to manhandle and too large to pass along passageways on board. This problem was solved by cutting temporary openings in the tweendeck steel bulkheads, welding a continuous steel runner bar along the underside of the beams and fitting each with a block and tackle. A cargo hatch was located at the fore end of the ship and so all the joinery units could be lowered by crane to the appropriate deck level, connected to the block and tackle and run down into their correct location. This then was the method used to outfit all the passenger cabins of *Vistafjord*.

Apart from the superstructure, the hull of the ship was built conventionally in prefabricated units, although the weight of these was restricted by the comparatively modest capacity of the shop and berth cranes. The superstructure however, was constructed entirely of aluminium and light cutting and welding equipment was purchased to handle this part of the work. Our welders received in-house training in the use of the welding equipment and there were no problems.

Karre Haug, the technical director of Norwegian Amerika Line was a naval architect of note and was at all times most friendly and helpful. I explained our outfitting system, in which he was interested, but emphasised that just as I needed our drawing office to work to a strict programme, the same principle would have to apply to the architects designing the public rooms. My Clydebank experience of such people had not been good. Karre Haug undertook to ensure that he finalised designs with the architects in good time for the architects to release their drawings to us.

In accordance with the programme, outfitting commenced in the crew accommodation on the lowest deck, together with the store rooms and baggage rooms located below. These were followed by blocks of passenger accommodation. By the time the ship was launched without ceremony in April 1972, 50% of the aluminium superstructure was erected and the crew cabins were 100% complete with the doors locked.

This novel method of outfitting began to pay dividends almost at once. By the time the joiners were allowed to commence their work in any block, most of the other outfit trades had moved on to the next, with the deck covering already completed. Joiners now gave full rein to their material handling system and their progress became quite astounding. The architects were pressurised by the owners and the only hold-up I recall in any public room area, concerned the dining room windows. More and more passenger blocks were being completed, while public rooms and main staircases were underway, all to programme. The last three months of outfitting was deeply satisfying. The momentum was now very great, while the beauty of the interior of the ship was becoming daily more apparent.

The ship was dry docked at Wallsend and ran successful sea trials off the Northumberland coast in February 1973. (*See illustration*) Handover and naming took place alongside Neptune jetty on 15th May 1973. The ship was complete in every respect and I knew of no skeleton in any cupboard.

Following the naming ceremony, cocktails and lunch were served on board and at 3.00 p.m. the ship sailed with a large party of owners and builders, together with wives, for an inaugural short voyage to Oslo, via Stavanger. Five hours were spent in Stavanger and before sailing more owners guests were embarked. At dawn on the 17th May, Norwegian Independence Day, the ship entered Oslofjord to a welcome by literally hundreds of small craft of every description, all waving Norwegian flags. This flotilla grew, the nearer we approached Oslo. As the ship berthed, brass bands were playing and fire tenders were spraying water high in the air.

As we flew over the vessel the following morning on our return journey, I reflected that this flagship of the Norwegian merchant marine, was without question, the finest ship that I had ever seen. Incidentally it is the last passenger liner to be constructed in the U.K.

The ship herself was designed specifically for cruising and was of 24,292 gross tons. With a length of 628 feet overall and a breadth of 82 feet, she was powered by two Sulzer diesel engines, each developing 12,000 B.H.P. to give a service speed of 20 knots. She was equipped with Denny-Brown fin stabilisers and a bow thruster to assist manoeuvring in harbour.

The ship was classified by Det Norske Veritas and complied with the latest rules of the Norwegian Maritime Directorate, the new

Successful sea trials off the Northumberland coast TSMV *Vistafjord*, February 1973.

rules of the International Convention of Safety of Life at Sea, U.S. Health and U.S. Coastguard. Elaborate arrangements in respect of fire detection and prevention, sewage and garbage handling and life-saving appliances were incorporated into the vessel. A vacuum cleaner plant was installed, consisting of two vacuum pumps located in the engine room, each operated by a 60 H.P. electric motor. From the cleaning tanks of this huge vacuum cleaner a network of pipes were routed through the entire ship.

The vessel was equipped with ten decks and accommodation was provided for 550 passengers and 390 officers and crew. This represented a particularly high ratio of crew to passengers and had been one of the factors leading to the vessel being consistently awarded top marks by international cruise consultants. The other factors were no doubt, the restrained elegance of the interior, the notably large public rooms and the unusually generous allocation of open deck space.

Apart from the dining room, located on the upper deck and the night club on the promenade deck, all the public rooms were located on the verandah deck. The garden lounge at the fore end of this deck, followed the half-round shape of the bridge front and was of a circular shape, with the centre section recessed into the deck below to form a small dance floor constructed of Greek marble. The deck height above this was increased by two feet to form a circular dome, with three steps in the ceiling. Concealed strip lighting was fitted into each step and a variety of different coloured lighting combinations effected by a small console located on the band podium. An upstand of marble was fitted around the perimeter of the dance floor into which exotic shrubs were planted. These shrubs growing up trellises, formed a natural division between the inner and outer sections of this lounge

A cinema, with seating for 235 persons was situated amidships immediately aft of the forward main staircase. The cinema was flanked on the port side by the North Cape bar and on the starboard side by the Norske lounge. Between these and the main ballroom were the "quiet" spaces — the library and writing room to port and the card rooms or "club 52" to starboard.

The main ballroom was located aft of the main hall and entered through glass doors. This very large and elegant room, stretching the full width of the ship, provided seating accommodation for the entire passenger capacity. Large windows were provided giving panoramic views, while the ballroom ended in a wide glass screen facing the outdoor cafe and swimming pool. The latter was arranged to be turned after dark into a lighted fountain. The lido deck, forming a teak surround to the swimming pool, was extensive in area and circular in shape.

On the sun and promenade decks, a number of extremely elegant suites were incorporated, the two largest being named, "King Haakon" and "King Olav". The rest of the passenger accommodation was located on upper, main and 'A' decks. All cabins were, without exception, large and 80% were on the outside of the ship. All had private facilities.

In an article devoted to the vessel, the Shipbuilding and Shipping Record in its publication of 25th May 1973, had this to say of the ship's construction — "The delivery of this complex ship, so far ahead of contract date, is a notable achievement and reflects the depth of advanced planning achieved by her builders. Swan Hunter kept a tight control of the time-consuming fitting-out work and only three of the ship's public rooms were sublet to private contractors. The overriding consideration in the vessel's construction has been the importance of being able to work on the public rooms and passenger accommodation at the earliest possible moment and the ship was sectionalised to this end. Much use of prefabrication was made in the outfitting, large cabin sections being built ashore. These were lowered into the ship through shafts left open in the verandah deck and a monorail system was built into each deck to take the sections to their final destination. There has been a very tight control of labour made possible as a result of this. All plumbing and wiring was finished before joiners moved into each section and much unnecessary work was saved as a result of this.

Vistafjord is a remarkable advertisement for the shipbuilding skills of Swan Hunter . . . . ."

So the bogey was finally laid to rest that U.K. shipbuilders were seemingly unable to deliver a passenger liner on time and in a finished condition.

CHAPTER 15

SMITHS DOCK CO. LTD.

PRIOR to delivery of *Vistafjord*, I was informed that I was to take up new duties as soon as the vessel was handed over. I was to become Managing Director of Smiths Dock Co. Ltd., at Southbank, Middlesbrough.

Southbank itself was a seedy run-down place, characterized by derelict land, old properties and crumbling jetties lying cheek by jowl with blast furnaces and engineering works. The shipyard looked across the murky River Tees to oil refineries with gas-flaring chimneys. Not far away lay I.C.I.'s two large works at Billingham and Wilton. The atmosphere was heavily polluted.

As noted elsewhere, this yard with its adjacent shiprepair facility, was run independently of the other yards in the Group. The facilities by modern shipyard standards were very poor. Little investment in plant and equipment had taken place, despite the fact that the company was making satisfactory profits. I was to learn very soon that all profit at the end of the financial year was transferred to the Group.

The yard was laid out with four berths equipped with travelling cranes, all but two being of ancient lineage. The steel working sheds were placed some distance from one another and so much material handling was necessary. The platers shed in particular, looked ready to fall down! The outfit shops were better equipped and were all located alongside or near the outfit jetty. The yard was capable of constructing ships up to about 35,000 tons deadweight. Shiprepairing was undertaken utilizing four graving docks immediately adjacent to the building berths. The dock gates leaked and the engineering shops were full of very old-fashioned equipment.

By contrast, my office was quite magnificent. It was said to be the best in the Group. I didn't doubt it! It measured I suppose some 40 feet in length and about 25 feet in width, with a high ceiling. In one corner stood a Cumberland stone fireplace, while a sofa and two easy chairs were placed in the centre of the room. My desk was at one end with the Board Room table and chairs at the other. I had a private toilet. Unfortunately in winter the pipes invariably froze.

The company had a really good order book, including six refrigerated ships ("reefers") for Island Fruit Reefers of Israel, two container ships for Manchester Lines Ltd. and three reefers for Blue Star Line Ltd. Shiprepair was reasonably busy.

The chairman of the board was Billy Straker-Smith, a member of the Swan Hunter Group board. Apart from board meetings and launches he seldom appeared in the yard and left me to run the business. I had reporting to me a Director for Production, for Finance, for Planning and for Shiprepair. But I had no Technical Director, because we had no Technical Department. All technical work was undertaken by the Drawing Office at the Haverton Hill shipyard, some distance up the river.

Smiths had entered into a licensing agreement with Drammen Slip & Verksted of Norway to build reefers of the so-called Drammen class. The initial order for eight reefers for Israel was based on this design. A similar agreement had been entered into with the Aker Group, also of Norway, in respect of the Blue Star order. Both agreements, particularly the latter, were costly but were fully reflected in the contract price for each vessel.

I had entered an entirely new phase of my working life, for no longer was I purely concerned with production matters. I had to learn to control a business and as the foregoing chapters have shown, I received no training, formal or otherwise to prepare me for such a role. Nor had I received any training in marketing or selling ships. But this duty fell exclusively to the Managing Director. Although "selling" was to become the most enjoyable part of 40 years in shipbuilding, the first three or four months were very difficult, as I tried to grasp the fundamentals of long-term, low fixed-interest credit arrangements, the role of the Export Credit Guarantee Department and other related matters. I was also trying to unravel the mysteries inherent in a ship's contract terms. It does seem to me now, that because none of these crucial matters had been explained before I was released into the unsuspecting world of commerce, a financial disaster could easily have occurred.

Then there was shiprepair, another new world to me. This area of operation was fully integrated with the shipbuilding operation and labour drawn from newbuildings as and when required. The company had developed a sideline in refinery maintenance and contracts were in force with both Shell at Teesport and Monsanto Chemicals at Greatham Sands.

I quickly discovered to my delight that despite the elderly plant and equipment, the labour force was highly productive. Moreover, labour relations were extremely good. There was still an air of the "family business" about the place, although some five years had elapsed since Swan Hunter Group had taken over from the Smiths. Probably this feeling was fostered by the fact that the company operated independently of the other yards. The reason for the independence was wages, which were high in relation to other Group yards. The fear was that if Smiths became part of Swan Hunter Shipbuilders Ltd., these high wage levels would prevail.

My earlier attempts to negotiate with shipowners were hesitant and in one case hilarious, although at the time I did not think so. We had received an enquiry from a London-based Greek shipowner for a bulk carrier. After a discussion in his City office, I said that in order to qualify for cheap credit backed by E.C.G.D., he would be required to pledge collateral. The owner told me to walk round the corner to his bank, one of the clearers, where the manager whom he named, would confirm the healthy state of his company bank balance. He added that he would telephone the manager before I reached the bank.

On arrival at the bank I asked for the manager, who wouldn't at first agree to see me. Eventually a sergeant-at-arms, led me along a corridor, unlocked the steel grille, opened a door and ushered me into the luxurious office of the manager. He sat behind a huge desk and looked extremely grim. He asked why I wished to see him. I explained, adding that by now his important client would have telephoned. He replied that he had received no such call, was not prepared to say whether the owner in question was the bank's client and furthermore had never heard of the proposed new ship, nor for that matter had he heard of Smiths Dock!

He implied that my sole purpose in seeing him was to learn the state of a client's account. I felt humiliated, but tried to give the impression of being someone with a fearfully quick temper and told him that this wasn't the last he would hear of this matter. In the end, things quietened down and he did concede that the Greek in question was a customer and promised to phone me the next day after speaking with his client. I duly received a very nice telex expressing his regret at what had transpired and confirming that his client had substantial sums on deposit with the bank. I never heard from the owner again!

The reefer market was reasonably buoyant and so, for a little time at least, orders were not too difficult to obtain. We received an enquiry from Blue Star Line for a further vessel, similar to the three already on order. I managed to negotiate a very good price for the steel required for this business and this "bargain" was explained to the owners. After a negotiation in the owner's offices I received a Letter of Intent to build Yard No. 1331 — m.v. *Almeda Star* — my first contract! Shortly afterwards and after a separate negotiation, we received another order for the *Almeria Star* (*See illustration* of sister ship MV *Afric Star*).

Meanwhile I was getting to know Manchester Liners personnel. Their superintendents and our technical people had between them designed container ships of the *Manchester Crusade* class, of which a number were in service and two further units were on order. They were custom-built for the owners service between Manchester and the St. Lawrence Seaway. The ships were the largest to navigate the Manchester Ship Canal and embodied quite a number of unique features.

The Manchester Liner board were extremely friendly and accessible. I invariably enjoyed my visits to their modern office block with its view overlooking "Coronation Street". The company was a wholly-owned subsidiary of Furness Withy and in this respect compared themselves to us, in relation to Swan Hunter Group. I gradually came to know the board very well, especially Tony Roberts the Managing Director, with whom I got on very good terms. From this point on, he kept me fully appraised of his company's future intentions insofar as newbuildings were concerned. I felt sure that we would in the future secure more business here. This proved to be the case.

Meanwhile in the yard, the Israeli reefers were forging ahead and

Blue Star Lines MV *Afric Star* at sea during sea trials, (sister ship of MV *Almeria Star*).

by the end of 1973, only two reefers of the original eight were left to launch, with two outfitting. I was becoming increasingly concerned however with the claims under guarantee that we were receiving from the four ships now in service. So I asked the owner's superintendent at the yard to discuss this matter. Alex Nimitz was a Bulgarian Jew, small, slight and alert. Unusually, he not only undertook the supervision of the hull construction of the vessels but also the machinery and refrigeration systems as well. He was a highly proficient little guy!

Included in the price of each ship was an allowance for guarantee repairs, equivalent to 1% of that price. The price of each ship was of the order of £3,000,000. Thus the allowance for guarantee was £30,000 approximately per ship. Four ships were still to deliver and thus a total allowance of £120,000 was still unused. The owners of course were unaware of these precise figures.

I explained my concern to Alex and suggested a "deal". His eyes immediately lit up, "Jews are always interested in deals", he said. After a negotiation it was agreed that I would deduct £28,000 from the final instalment of the price due on delivery of the last four ships and in return, he would ensure that with immediate effect, we would receive no more claims for any of the eight vessels. For this to be implemented he suggested a brokerage fee of £1,000 (to himself). Everyone kept his word!

In the months that followed, I began to relish the marketing and selling aspects of shipbuilding. More orders were placed. Blue Star Line, with whom we were now on excellent terms, formed a new company called Star Offshore Services, which would operate a fleet of offshore supply boats for North Sea service. An order was placed for two pipe carriers. Meanwhile Manchester Liners placed an order for a pair of beautiful 20-knot container ships — the *Manchester Vanguard* and *Manchester Venture* (*See illustrations*). These were of a new class and could accommodate 946-20-foot containers.

I was not travelling abroad much at this time but I continued to market hard in the City of London and elsewhere in the U.K., particularly with reefer owners, such as Shaw Savill & Albion, Fyffe's Group and P. & O.

Labour relations remained good, although problems did arise from time to time. On one occasion I recall being brought into the discussions with the Boilermakers' local delegate. The atmosphere

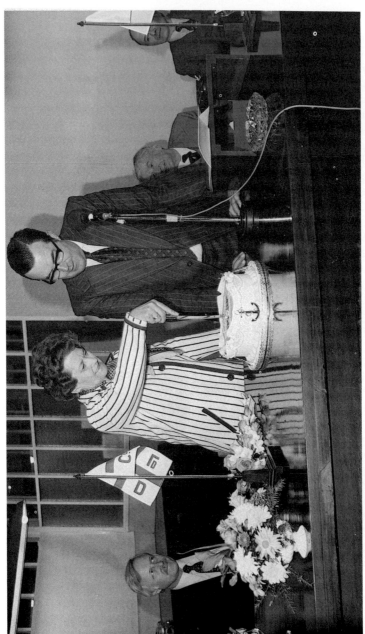

"Cutting the christening cake". Commissioning of MV *Manchester Vanguard* at Southbank, 1977.

MV *Manchester Vanguard* ready for commissioning and handover at Southbank, 13th October 1977.

became heated until finally, keeping the malapropism tradition of delegates alive, I was told — "I'm absolutely incest with your remarks!"

At the end of the first financial year for which I was responsible, we made a Trading Profit of £1,000,000 on a Turnover of some £20,000,000. After the accounts had been audited an internal transaction followed under which all but £5,000 was transferred to H.Q. We never saw it again in the form of new plant and machinery or anything else.

By 1975, I had become concerned about one aspect of the company's activities. This was our lack of an in-house Design and Drawing Office facility. It was true that we had taken orders for a series of eight reefer ships, followed by another series of five, by paying a big licence fee for the availability of the design information and drawings. But I felt that to rely heavily on obtaining future orders on such a basis was costly. More importantly, if and when the market turned down, then the fewer orders that became available might never be placed with us, since the licensors would, in these circumstances, not extend our licence.

The Swan Hunter yards on the Tyne and Tees were capable of building almost every kind of ship and this of course included reefers. But because we had built or were building thirteen ships of this type, Swan's left us to follow up enquiries for such vessels. Indeed they sometimes passed their enquiries for reefers to us. But for virtually all other classes of ship, we were not supposed to compete with Swan's, although there had never been any formal agreement to this effect. I did not fancy limiting Smith's to building purely reefer ships, since to do so would surely dry up the order book. These factors led me to the conclusion that we had to:—

    a) Develop our own design of a vessel other than a reefer and

    b) This vessel had to be seen as not competing with Swan's.

Despite the weakness of the technical facility on which I was obliged to rely, I felt certain that we had to extend our product range, utilising our own design. Thus was born the Smiths Dock 7,500 ton deadweight Roll-on, Roll-off freight carrier. Swan Hunter had only built one large Ro-Ro ship, one of a series built by a number of builders. I hoped that a modest sized Ro-Ro vessel would not conflict with the Group's interests.

Of course the features of the new design could only be established after a certain amount of market research. Container ships are only viable if appropriate container terminals and infrastructure are in place at both the loading and discharge ports. Such facilities were increasingly coming on stream in the developed countries. But in the Third-World countries, neither the infrastructure, nor the finance to construct the terminals, was available. The interim solution for such countries was the cargo Ro-Ro ship. Such vessels require somewhat modest shore facilities. Many of the ports involved had a draught limitation. I wanted a design that could find favour in many ports of the world, as well as being modest in price. All this pointed to a smallish Ro-Ro vessel.

We eventually produced a design for a twin-screw cargo Ro-Ro vessel of 7,500 tons deadweight with a service speed of 18 knots and able to accommodate 1,500 trailer metres. Its asking price was around £8,000,000. I approached Richard Bright, a shipbroker friend of mine and enquired if his company would be interested in marketing the vessel World-wide. This offer was snapped up and soon telexes were being sent out to shipowners as far apart as Brazil and Hong Kong.

At this point, we received an enquiry from Blue Star Line in respect of small heavy-lift ships. Two vessels were required by a new company set up jointly by Blue Star and Sloman-Neptun of West Germany. After a good deal of negotiation, the two vessels were placed, one with Martin Jansen of Leer in West Germany and the other with us. The price was agreed and so was the specification and I had a Letter of Intent. To my surprise, some days later I was asked to go to Bremen for a meeting with the joint owners. We met in a beautiful conference room in the Park Hotel. Sloman-Neptun, Blue Star, Martin Jansen and Smiths Dock were all represented. In the chair was a director of Sloman-Neptun, who at precisely 9.00 a.m. opened the proceedings by announcing in English the agenda thus:—

Item 1 — Negotiation of Smiths Dock price.

Item 2 — Negotiation of Martin Jansens price.

and thereafter twelve or so other items.

All this was stated in a quite aggressive tone. Before proceeding further he asked for any comments.

I stated slowly and distinctly that so far as we were concerned

Item 1 was not negotiable. I did not propose to discuss our agreed price further and sat down. To my surprise, the chairman accepted this without demur and the owners calmly went on to discuss Martin Jansen's price in front of us!

In 1976 the Government finally decided to Nationalise the industry and appointed Graham Day, Chief-Executive-Designate of the future British Shipbuilders. An "organising committee" was formed under Graham Day to undertake preliminary work. Some shiprepairers in particular were very unhappy about the prospect of nationalisation and managed to delay the Shipbuilding Industry Bill being placed on the Statute Book by many months. As a result, Graham Day resigned and returned to Canada. His place was taken by Michael Casey, who as a civil servant had been in charge of the Shipbuilding Policy Division at the Department of Trade and Industry.

Towards the end of 1976, we managed to clinch an order for two of our Ro-Ro ships from Ellerman Wilson Line of Hull, a subsidiary of Ellerman Lines Ltd. At about the same time, we were negotiating with Blue Star for two reefer container ships and seemed likely to obtain these. But because of our own current workload, including the two Ro-Ro ships, we were unable to meet the delivery dates required by Blue Star.

I explained this to Tom McIver, who immediately announced that he wished me to conclude negotiations with Blue Star and hopefully secure the contracts on the basis that the required deliveries could be maintained by building both vessels in the Haverton Hill shipyard. He proposed in addition, that Swan Hunter Shipbuilders sell the Haverton Hill yard to Smiths and henceforth it would come under my command.

While feeling flattered by this proposal, I was not a little worried. Haverton Hill had at that point very little work in hand and from what I had heard on the grapevine, industrial relations might prove difficult. But at least we would now have our own Technical Department.

In due course all was agreed with the owners, who nonetheless had reservations about their ships being built at Haverton Hill, a yard they did not know. They also agreed to allow me to subcontract the hull construction of the small heavy-lift ship to Swan Hunter and outfit the vessel at Haverton Hill. This was necessary because of the Southbank workload. The Southbank labour force were furious at losing three ships from owners whom they regarded as "their" best customer.

In 1977, the Shipbuilding Industry Bill was finally placed on the statute book and Vesting date for British Shipbuilders was set for 1st July. The boards of the various companies to be nationalised entered into negotiations with Government concerning the compensation to be paid for their assets. I now began to understand why Swan Hunter had been so keen for me to conclude the business with Blue Star Line. Without these ships, Swan Hunter would have begun these negotiations with one yard totally bereft of work. The fact that it was a "going concern" I am sure improved the compensation paid to the Group.

On 1st July 1977 we became Smiths Dock Co Ltd., — a member of British Shipbuilders. I wondered if I had not come this way before!

CHAPTER 16

SMITHS DOCK CO. LTD. POST-NATIONALISATION

ALL the Naval and larger Merchant Shipbuilding Companies, some of the Shiprepairers and Marine Enginebuilders were now under the umbrella of the Corporation. Including staff, the total number employed was 87,000. Only a small rump was left under private ownership.

For the first few months, our existence carried on much as it had been prior to Vesting day. But plenty was afoot elsewhere. After much speculation and lobbying about where the H.Q. should be located, we learned that two sites were to be utilized — one near the centre of Newcastle and the other in London. Benton House at Newcastle was an extensive new office block. The new office block in Knightsbridge, although smaller, could hardly have been chosen in a more expensive location and was some distance from the City of London, wherein were located the centres of Banking, Broking and Shipowning activities within the U.K.

The Board was appointed and thereafter faces started rapidly appearing in the various offices. Benton House became the Registered Office and was to house all H.Q. personnel except for marketing staff. The board members had offices in each location. Each was appointed by the Secretary of State for Trade and Industry. I saw little of any of them, except when called to fortnightly meetings in London of all Chief Executives within the Corporation. The numbers involved required the use of a large conference room, which could be readily provided by a number of first class hotels in the West End of London. For the next few months it seemed that the Chief Executives were being taken on a grand tour of high-class London hotels. We were certainly able to compare notes about their differing, but equally appetizing menus.

Smiths Dock had turned in Trading Profits averaging £900,000 for the 4 financial years prior to nationalisation. But we got off to a very poor start from 1st July 1977 for a number of reasons. Firstly, labour relations at Haverton Hill was, from the outset, a "can of worms". Hardly a week passed without either an overtime ban or a stoppage or a claim for increased allowances. The Blue Star ships programme became seriously affected.

Meanwhile the little heavy-lift ship had been built on Tyneside and towed to Haverton Hill for outfitting. Nearing completion a strike occurred and since the ship was fixed for a very lucrative charter, we had to arrange to have the ship towed away from the yard and have it completed elsewhere. The actual removal took place at dead of night. Had this arrangement not been made, the ship would most certainly have lost its charter.

The Blue Star container ships were to inaugurate a new service from Australia and New Zealand to Middle East ports carrying frozen meat. The sponsor selected for each vessel was the wife of a prominent Australian and New Zealand politician and because of this, I had to agree a launch date for each vessel earlier than I would have wished. In one of our many skirmishes with the Haverton Hill shop stewards, I extracted a solemn promise that both V.I.P. launches would take place as planned.

Two days before the launch of *Australia Star* in January 1978, the boilermakers imposed an overtime ban. In the event, the ship could only be named but not physically launched. The sponsor and her party had flown all the way from Canberra for this!

On 20th July 1978, Mrs. Muldoon, wife of the New Zealand Prime Minister, was on her way up to Teesside by train from Kings Cross, accompanied by a large owners' party. This time the ship was ready with only the remaining blocks to knock out. The launch was timed for 4.00 p.m. At 11.00 a.m. I was informed that all 750 boilermakers had walked out on strike but would return provided that a substantial and immediate increase in wages was offered by management.

After venting my wrath upon the shop stewards concerned, I telephoned from Haverton Hill to the Chairman of the Southbank

Foremans Committee and explained the crisis. The time was around midday. The blocks under the ship had to start coming out no later than 1.00 p.m. if the ship was to launch at 4.00 p.m., just before high water. The reaction was unbelievably swift and effective. The Committee gathered a number of foremen together, abandoned their lunch, hired a coach and some forty or so foremen arrived at Haverton Hill a few minutes before 1.00 p.m. They were armed with sledgehammers, steel wedges and other gear needed for the removal of the blocks.

The owner's party duly arrived and the ship was launched without any problems. I should perhaps mention here that of the forty or so foremen who prepared the ship for launch, only a few were shipwrights with experience of such work. On the way back to the reception in the offices following the launch, I explained to the owners the excitement of the last few hours. I invited the Southbank foremen to join the launch reception and they all crowded in near the doorway still dressed in their overalls. The entire launch party rose to their feet and toasted the foremen with champagne. The foremen got their share of course. I resolved privately at that moment to close down the Haverton Hill shipyard. It had become a complete liability and would, if allowed to continue, drag down Smiths Dock, Southbank, as well.

Another reason we got off to a poor start after Nationalisation concerned the Ro-Ro vessels building at Southbank. This type of vessel was of course new to us and during the development of the structural plans, Lloyd's Register insisted on considerable additions to the steel structure. Moreover, when the construction got underway, we made heavy weather of the prefabrication and erection of the units. As a result, both material and labour costs in respect of steelwork exceeded those allowed in the contract price.

Nearing completion of the first vessel in the Spring of 1978, we ran into more problems. The contractor who had supplied and installed the internal cargo "scissor lift" could not succeed in making it function properly. Much more serious was the fact that on trials the ship had not achieved its contract speed. This was most unusual because all new hull designs are tested in a "model tank", where wax models are both towed and propelled at ballast and load draughts to establish the contract speed. In our case, after adjustments had been made to the model and the tests re-run, we were advised that 18 knots would be achieved with the ship in service. I had not previously heard of a single case where the "tank prediction" had been far wrong. But here we were with about half a knot less than contract speed. Penalty clauses existed in the contract, on a sliding scale basis — the lower the speed, the heavier the penalty, until a point is reached below which the owner may opt to determine the contract. In May 1978 m.v. *Cicero* was delivered somewhat late having involved us in penalties as well as cost overruns.

In November 1978 the sister vessel *Cavallo* ran trials and was nearing handover. She too had failed of course to achieve 18 knots contract speed. A little later and without any warning our company received a Writ from the owners, alleging breach of contract on account of speed deficiency. The owners further alleged that on the first vessel, much damage had been caused by trailers breaking loose from their lashings. They also alleged that certain Port Authorities considered the scissor lift dangerous. Accordingly, they refused to accept delivery of *Cavallo* and demanded the return of instalments paid plus interest. Fortunately for us, under the terms of the contract, 85% of the contract price of £8,500,000 had been paid in instalments prior to delivery. So we had the ship and 85% of the money! The matter was to take years to settle, as we shall see.

Yet another reason contributing to our poor financial showing following vesting was the Manchester Liner container ships. These vessels were built without any problems and the second vessel delivered towards the end of 1977. Unfortunately, our Design Office had badly underestimated the steelweight of the ships. The shortfall involved could not be recovered from the owners and the cost of the additional steel and labour had to be absorbed.

Naturally, the effect of all of these major problems was to cause the company to record a thumping loss for the first and second years of Nationalisation.

While all these problems were demanding our attention, the shipping market was very poor and orders very scarce. A number of merchant shipbuilders in the Corporation were becoming very short of work, including us. It was at this point that the Government embarked on a scheme designed to secure orders for a large number of handy-sized bulk carriers, a few small bulk carriers and two crane barges, all for Poland. Twenty-four units in all were involved. I did not take part in any of the discussions or negotiations, but there was much "to-ing and fro-ing" between Knightsbridge, Benton House and Poland. The deal was extremely complex and I am told that although the vessels were completed some 10 years ago, the British tax payer is still paying for the consequences. At the time however, relief was felt at the prospect of more work.

On completion of the lengthy negotiations, B.S. allocated the ships to various yards. At this point we were not among them. Swan Hunter, who had been allocated a number of vessels were suffering severe problems at the time, at the hands of the boilermakers. Michael Casey, the B.S. Chief Executive, eventually issued an ultimatum to the employees concerned, to the effect that the allocation of the vessels was conditional upon resolving the dispute by a given date. Their failure to do so resulted in a reallocation of the vessels. Smiths Dock was very pleased to be allocated two handy-sized bulk carriers.

Meanwhile, as at Upper Clyde Shipbuilders, the Unions had not been idle. In the late '70s, under the terms of Article XI of the Fair Wages Act, legitimate claims were lodged by individual trades for parity with the highest paid of these trades within the Corporation. Similar claims were lodged on behalf of staff. In the case of the latter, the increases awarded at Smiths Dock were truly astronomical!

While the two Polish vessels awarded to Smiths Dock was welcome news, there was nothing to follow them. New contracts remained extremely hard to obtain. I had long cast envious eyes at Sunderland Shipbuilders' close relationship with Andrew Weir and Co. Ltd. (the Bank Line). These owners of high-standing were the only remaining U.K. shipowner never to have ordered abroad. They ordered all their cargo vessels from Sunderland Shipbuilders — often in threes and sometimes in sixes! I knew Captain Brian Rodgers, their Marine Superintendent, through our shiprepairing interests and from time-to-time called on him in the Bank Line offices in the City of London.

On one such visit early in 1978, he advised me that a new service was to be inaugurated between Australia and the Western and Eastern Seaboards of the U.S.A. for the carriage of refrigerated cargoes in containers. A new company was to be set up jointly by Furness Withy and Bank Line to own and operate these custom-built vessels.

We duly received the enquiry and then began a long but extremely pleasant series of negotiations between both owners and ourselves. Swan Hunter was also bidding for the ships, as were some others. A Government subsidy called the "Intervention Fund" had been available for some time to all U.K. builders — indeed both the Blue Star and Ellerman Ships had benefited from this Fund. The Corporation employed a small in-house team to administer the Fund in conjunction with the Department of Trade and Industry. It was imperative to have the support of this team for any contracts to be obtained. In this case, they were prepared to support both Swan Hunter and ourselves on the basis that if successful we would each build one ship.

I learned with great amusement a little later, that at the point when contracts were to be announced in September 1978, both the Chairman of Furness Withy and Bank Line wanted their ship to be built by Smiths Dock. They finally tossed for it and Lord Inverforth of Bank Line won! One of my ambitions had been satisfied — I had an order from the Bank Line. This turned out to be a very happy association.

But we had only three ships on order, so I determined to market abroad. In November 1978 I followed up an enquiry for a reefer vessel in Sarasota, on the Gulf Coast of Florida and thereafter visited a Dutch owner of reefer ships in Tampa. Nothing doing in either camp. I then teamed up with a Corporation marketing manager and flew to Mexico where a shipping exhibition was in progress. There we arranged to see two shipowners. We again drew a blank.

Back in Middlesbrough, *New Zealand Star* was handed over to Blue Star Line at the end of January 1979. Shortly afterwards and with the prior agreement of the Corporation, Haverton Hill shipyard was closed. Token resistance was offered by local M.P.s and union officials. Since no work was available for the yard, there was nothing they could do to prevent the closure. Not a tear was shed by the Southbank labour force! As a direct result of this closure, the Corporation approved our application for capital expenditure to construct a Design and Drawing Office adjacent to our existing offices at Southbank.

In the early Spring of 1979, we learned of the interest of Geest Line in constructing two or possibly four reefers for their service between Barry, South Wales and the Windward Islands of the Caribbean. The ships would each accommodate twelve passengers. The existing vessels on this service had been built by the Greenock Dockyard Co. Ltd., which had been absorbed by Scotts of Greenock before their merger with Lithgows. Ross Belch, my old boss at Lithgows Ltd. (and recently knighted) was now Managing Director of the Scott-Lithgow Group and it was he who first intimated the intentions of Geest. He suggested a joint approach and in March 1979 we had our opening discussion with the owners in their offices in Spalding, Lincolnshire. It seemed a most unlikely place for a shipowner to locate his H.Q. In fact of course, Geest were primarily horticulturists, but in a big way and the area around Spalding was their "seed-bed".

Thus began a long and for me, not especially agreeable negotiation. We visited Spalding on a number of occasions and it gradually became clear that the price that Scott-Lithgow needed to break even and this dictated the criteria for the subsidy from Government to be paid, was a bit higher than that required by us. Since other foreign shipbuilders were stated to be quoting, I felt that to quote on the basis of even a median price — a halfway house between the Scott-Lithgow figure and ours — could run the risk of losing the business. Two things happened to resolve the issue. First, the Corporation Intervention Fund Staff considered that the overall funds available from Government should be disbursed in the most economical manner. Accordingly they decided that they could not support Scott-Lithgow's application for a subsidy, but only ours. Second, Geest decided to restrict the number of newbuildings to two. After further lengthy negotiations we contracted with Geest Line for two vessels in March 1980. The negotiations had spanned exactly one year!

The Chairman of the Corporation, Admiral Sir Anthony Griffin, led two teams abroad during the year. I was included in both of them. The first trip was to Algiers, where the B.S. Marketing Department had established that the Algerian National Shipping Line could be interested in ordering Ro-Ro ships and their Navy in ordering small naval vessels. The visit was interesting but fruitless.

On the first evening, the Algerians laid on a party at a local hotel.

They could only speak French. We began circulating among our hosts before dinner and visiting cards were exchanged as a hopeful start to some broken and in my case pathetic, French. A large man with a huge smile approached and handed me his card. On it was written, "Monsieur Hi-Hi". Politely I said, "Bonsoir, Monsieur High-High". Still smiling he replied "Non, non, Monsieur Hee-Hee".

A little later Mr. Hi-Hi led me into the adjoining room where we split into groups of about six or seven people. A whole sheep, legs and all, roasting on a spit, was wheeled into the centre of each group. Mr. Hi-Hi motioned for me to pick the first handful! I did so and withdrew my hand hastily. It was red hot! Thereafter Mr, Hi-Hi personally fed me!

Before our departure two days later our hosts laid on a luncheon on board one of their Ro-Ro vessels — champagne and a very good buffet. Before taking our leave we were each presented with a "beaten" copper tray. Our Chairman was presented with a large brown paper parcel. Inside was a cloak made from camel hair. It looked positively unhygienic! The Chairman donned the cloak which reached to the ground and standing so attired, with a cigar in one hand and a glass of champagne in the other, turned to me with a grin and said, "What do you think of this then?". I could only think of saying, "Chairman, I think you look like a cross between a camel-dealer and a Professor of Arabic Studies!".

The second trip was to Australia in April 1979. So far as I was concerned, my inclusion in the party was a mistake! There was at that time a possibility of orders from the Australian Navy. The Chief Executives of both Vickers and Yarrows, together with other Executives in the Corporation concerned with Naval building made up the bulk of the party. I was the only pure Merchant Shipbuilder included, but my role was not to market merchant ships but to market semi-submersible drilling vessels — a subject I knew next to nothing about! To this day, I never discovered why no-one in the Offshore Division of British Shipbuilders was not instructed to join the team instead of me.

The offshore oil industry in Australia is based at Perth in Western Australia while the Australian Naval Staff is based at Canberra. Merchant shipowners were mostly to be found at Melbourne. The plan was for me to accompany the party as far as

Canberra, stay overnight, then "peel off" alone to Melbourne, visit some shipowners for one day, then again alone, fly to Perth to visit offshore operators. I enjoyed my discussions in Melbourne with a number of shipowners and thereafter left for the airport for the long flight to Perth.

En-route, I had an engaging conversation with an amusing Australian doctor. After a time he asked — "Have you been to Perth before?" I replied — "Hundreds of times". "Really, do you come from Kalgoorli?" he asked. "No, Dundee", I replied.

I managed, not without difficulty, to carry out my brief with offshore operators. I made contact with the Trade Counsellor in the U.K. Embassy and he showed me around Perth — a truly beautiful city. After three days, it was time for the long flight home via Bombay. Incidentally — London back to London in seven days!

During 1979 also, we had discussions with Moroccans in connection with their interest in building small reefers for the carriage of citrus fruit. In addition, we treated extremely seriously the enquiry from Trinity House for the replacement of their flag ship *Patricia*. Curiously enough, the ship that was to be replaced had been built by Smiths Dock as far back as 1937! So it must have been well built! A number of British yards were tendering together with one West German yard. The competition was fierce but eventually three yards were left in the hunt — the West German yard, Robb-Caledon and us. There were those in Trinity House who hoped we would be awarded the contract. Indeed we did most of the design work and were instructed to issue the information to the other British Shipbuilders' yards who were tendering. I was confident we would win and was dumbfounded when I learned that the Chairman had publicly announced the order for Robb-Caledon. Furious, I rang him in London and asked him if this was true and demanded to know how a decision to award the contract to Robb-Caledon had been arrived at. The Chairman replied — "These negotiations have been going on for a long time and we just decided to go for the corner flag". I couldn't stop myself from saying — "It's a pity you weren't carrying the bloody ball!".

It was now three years since vesting and all this marketing and selling I have described had only resulted in orders for one ship from the Bank Line and two from Geest, apart of course from the two Polish ships. This may explain my anger at losing the Trinity House vessel.

Up to now I have only described what was happening in Smiths Dock — the ships, the problems, the losses, marketing and selling. Over this same period, British Shipbuilders had not begun to change our modus operandi to any great extent, although this would shortly alter. We were called to Chief Executives' meetings of course. I was placed on the Capital Expenditure Committee. We were also called to a series of Budget Meetings each year in preparation for the production of the Corporate Plan. But "down at t'mill" we were left surprisingly to ourselves. On the occasions we were called to Benton House or Knightsbridge however, we noted great changes.

It seemed that on entering either H.Q. we left the real world behind. The atmosphere was very relaxed and by now there were a great many people occupying Benton House. The Finance Department had swelled to include Cost Accountants, Tax Experts and a variety of clerks and secretaries. The Industrial Relations Department had similarly expanded with executives designated to deal with labour relations, productivity services, staff salaries and appraisals. A small Legal Department was in place. The Corporation had a statutory duty under the Shipbuilding Act (1977) to produce each year, a five year Corporate Plan. This document ran to 60 or 70 pages and reviewed all aspects of the Corporation's affairs over the previous year and made financial forecasts for the next four years based on market assumptions, price assumptions and ordering assumptions. All this required the input of every subsidiary. Each was required to submit a four year budget which was then discussed endlessly at meetings at Benton House. This dreary tome was finalised in the month of May and sent to Government. I doubt if anyone of real influence had either the time or the inclination to read it. But what the small staff dedicated to the production of this document did for the rest of the year remains a mystery to me!

The same totally relaxed atmosphere was evident at Knightsbridge where the Marketing Department was based, both for shipbuilding and shiprepair. Some ten people were involved plus secretaries. They visited countries like Djibouti and Angola for example, whose economies were quite unable to finance the construction of ships. On their return from their travels, we would all receive glowing reports of the potential business merely waiting to be scooped up by the Corporation!

The Corporation was now recording huge losses each year despite the profits being made by the Naval builders. There were rumours that the Government would shortly privatise the naval yards and that prospect filled me with alarm.

I have already mentioned how the unions had secured for their members, including staff, big increases under the terms of the Fair Wages Act. But this was quite separate from the annual ritual of wage bargaining. Each year the Confederation of Shipbuilding and Engineering Unions met the Chairman and other Executives of the Corporation at Benton House and formally presented a claim. The Chairman of the Confederation was John Chalmers, General Secretary of the Boilermakers Union, whom incidentally I had known since my Clyde Shipbuilders Association days. He had served his apprenticeship at Clydebank as a plater.

This particular year he led into the Board Room a large deputation of union officials together with a collection of shop stewards, a number of whom looked as if they had not slept very well. On our side of the table sat our Chairman, Ken Griffin the Deputy Chairman and himself an ex-Union official, the Industrial Relations Director of the Corporation and his staff, together with a number of yard Chief Executives. Our Chairman invited John Chalmers to present his claim. To my horror, he opened approximately as follows — "Thank you Mr. Chairman but before I present our claim today. I want to refer to an incident that occurred some months ago at the Haverton Hill shipyard. A V.I.P. launch was about to take place. A few hours before the launch, our members, I regret to say, took unconstitutional action and walked out on strike. George Parker sent for the shop stewards concerned. No doubt he felt severely provoked, but that can't excuse what he said to them, which was — 'P - - - off!'. He's nothing more than a Victorian employer! I now come to the main reason for this meeting — our claim . . .".

John Chalmers finished at last and our Chairman responded. Tony Griffin was an immensely likeable man with impeccable manners. His naval training had no doubt taught him to be very precise. He had taken copious notes throughout the presentation of the claim. He replied, approximately as follows — "Thank you John, for your helpful and constructive remarks. I have noted all the various points and propose to have my colleagues reply to each in the order in which they appeared in your presentation". Turning to me he said "I think George that you were mentioned first — would you care to reply?".

I felt like advising John Chalmers that his remarks were anything but helpful and constructive and that his ex-shop stewards at Haverton Hill had consistently flouted procedure. Instead I said, — "John Chalmers has called me a Victorian employer. If by that he means I am someone who expects eight hours of work for eight hours pay, than I'm proud to be called, Victorian".

In 1980 after the Geest contract had been signed, we only had the Bank Line ship underway. Marketing continued as hard as ever. Discussions began in March with British and Commonwealth in respect of two reefers. These looked promising, but at the last minute B & C's partners — Saf (Marine) of South Africa pulled out and the project was dead. Later in the year, we responded to an enquiry from the Central Electricity Generating Board in respect of colliers to carry coal from the Northeast Coast to River Thames Power Stations. A number of B.S. yards were in the running, but the Corporation finally directed the order to Govan Shipbuilders. The year closed with no further orders secured. For much of 1980 however, I was diverted by our old friend *Cavallo*, which was still lying alongside the jetty 100% complete.

B.S. Legal Department, with whom I became increasingly involved concerning our response to the Writ, advised me that I was perfectly free to sell the vessel. Some little time afterwards we learned from a London shipbroker that a Bulgarian shipping line might be interested in purchasing the vessel. A visit was quickly arranged to Sofia — behind the Iron Curtain. The visit was unsuccessful and I was relieved when the time came to fly home. Throughout our short visit we were accompanied at all times by a gentleman who was referred to as Popoff Protocol — the name sounded sinister.

We then learned from a marketing manager employed by Vosper Thornycroft that the Indonesian Navy could be interested in having the vessel converted for the carriage of tanks and other military equipment. We arranged to meet him in Singapore and together flew on to Djakarta. We spent a number of days in this humid place. We were first introduced to a large Dutchman, who "knew" the Admirals involved with the procurement of ships. After meeting those involved we learned that the commissions payable to the

Dutchman, the two serving and one retired Admirals was to amount to no less than 7½% of the price of the ship! The fact that we proposed to charge the Indonesian Navy £15,000,000 for the ship (including modifications) only made the so-called commissions even higher. I was again relieved that we had been unsuccessful in our objective, since I would have had a problem in trying to explain to the Corporation and to our auditors how a figure of well in excess of £1,000,000 could possibly be charged for brokerage!

We had other abortive attempts to sell the ship, but finally it was sold to Fed Nav of Canada for a very low price. I was then advised by our Legal Department to remit to Ellermans the cash that we had received in excess of the original £8,500,000 contract price, less of course, all our marketing and maintenance expenses. As a footnote, I should add that these new owners were so satisfied with *Cavallo* in service that they later chartered the sister ship!

In January 1981, three of us flew to New York and called on United Brands (the parent company of Fyffes in the U.K.), Reefer Express lines and other owners. The temperature was minus 17° F. We got no more than a flicker of interest. We then flew to Montreal (the temperature here was minus 23° F) and called on Fed Nav and Canada Steamship Lines. We had interesting discussions with both, but nothing developed. We got a bit of a fright on the first morning in Montreal. We were staying at the Four Seasons Hotel where my two colleagues had been allocated rooms on the 28th floor. I was allocated a room on the 29th.

The following morning, I had just stepped out of the shower cubicle, when a very loud fire-alarm went off and kept on ringing. I thought at first it was a false alarm and decided to put my head round the bedroom door to check. I smelled smoke! Only days before, during the Christmas holiday, I had watched a really gripping film called "Towering Inferno" all about a big hotel fire!

Such situations certainly concentrate the mind on what to wear and what belongings to take! I was dressed in "nothing but a smile". I grabbed a bath towel and wrapped it round me, donned a raincoat, stepped into shoes and remembered my passport and door key. Fortunately the door to the fire escape was nearby and everyone on the 29th floor converged on it and began descending the staircase. More and more guests emerged from the lower floors as we made our slow progress downwards. Eventually, on the 12th floor, we saw the entire corridor full of black acrid smoke. Then we were passed it to safety.

In the lobby, I saw my two colleagues fully dressed. They had got up earlier than I (there must be a moral in this somewhere!). I saw only one other guest attired in less clothes than I. He too was wearing a raincoat, but was barefooted. So relieved to be at ground level, I said to this perfect stranger — "What about a quick flash?". At least he wore a towel! Fire brigades began to arrive, including one equipped with a turntable ladder, but it reached only to the 8th floor! The fire was quickly extinguished. Two rooms had been gutted. We were eventually allowed to return to our rooms where I collected my credit cards. They were exactly where I had left them!

Earlier in 1980, Michael Casey had been succeeded by Robert Atkinson. Later in the year, Sir Anthony Griffin retired and from that point Robert Atkinson became Chairman as well as Chief Executive. He made it clear from the start that he meant business. It didn't seem to take him long to absorb the considerable data with which he must have been presented, covering all aspects of the Corporation's affairs. He visited Smiths in October.

Without warning, in April 1981, I was advised that I was to be transferred to B.S. Shiprepair Division as its Managing Director. I was surprised and not very pleased at the prospect. But the Chairman promised that he would return me to Merchant Shipbuilding in due course. I took up my new duties on 11th May 1981.

CHAPTER 17

SHIPREPAIR DIVISION
(See illustration)

WHEN the industry was nationalised in 1977 all shipbuilding companies, Naval and Merchant, were vested in the Corporation, except for a handful of companies building very small merchant vessels. Accordingly, in the U.K. at least most B.S. yards had no competition. Not so in shiprepairing.

A number of shiprepairing companies remained in private hands. They were situated in various locations including Tyneside, Wearside, Humberside, Southampton, South Wales and Clydeside. Shipbuilders and shiprepairers in the private sector had set up an association called the "Shipbuilders and Shiprepairers Independent Association" (S.S.I.A.) to act as their mouthpiece on any matters of common concern.

Thus B.S. Shiprepair Division not only suffered foreign competition but U.K. competition as well. The Division itself consisted of four companies located at Tyneside, Grangemouth, Southampton and Falmouth. I became Chairman of all four.

The largest of these was Tyne Shiprepair Ltd., (T.S.L.), whose Head Office was at South Shields. The company was an amalgam of a number of ex-privately owned shiprepairers on the River Tyne — Mercantile Drydocks, Brigham & Cowan and Middle Docks, all on the south side of the river and Wallsend Drydocks on the north side. The facilities of the first two were by this time rarely used. To all intents and purposes therefore, T.S.L. shiprepairing was carried out at Middle Docks at South Shields with four drydocks and at

Shiprepairing at Tyne Shiprepair Ltd., May 1981.

Wallsend also with four drydocks. They employed at this time some 900/1,000 people. When insufficient work was available and this was quite frequently, the numbers of men for whom work could not be found were sent home on an "idle time" allowance. This was a very costly arrangement and applied to all B.S. shiprepair yards.

Grangemouth Dockyard Ltd., (G.D.L), was a tiny shiprepair facility located on the River Carron, a tributory of the River Forth, some fifteen or so miles west of Edinburgh. It had two small drydocks and employed fewer than 100 people.

Vospers Shiprepairers Ltd., (V.S.L.), was a shiprepair facility located within the Southampton Dock complex. Two drydocks were available, one of which was situated adjacent to the offices and shops. The other, the so-called "Queen Elizabeth Dock", was over 1,000 feet in length and was owned by the Port Authority. The company in addition, owned the Northam Yard, a separate small facility equipped with a patent slipway. The company employed some 600/700 people.

Falmouth Shiprepair Ltd., (F.S.L.), was located close to the centre of Falmouth. Its large acreage contained four drydocks, extensive jetties and shops. It employed some 400 people.

I had barely time to visit these four companies before the Chairman demanded to see me. He showed me a letter he had just received from the Secretary of State for Trade and Industry. The letter referred to allegations made by the S.S.I.A. in connection with repair work recently won by T.S.L. The S.S.I.A. claimed that T.S.L. had cut their price to the bone and the S.S.I.A. believed that the contract would turn out to be a loss maker. The S.S.I.A. went on to suggest to the Secretary of State that if their members chose to cut their prices in order to obtain work, the loss incurred could only be absorbed by the company and ultimately its shareholders. Not so with B.S. shiprepair yards, where a similar tab would be picked up by the taxpayer.

The Chairman demanded an immediate investigation and a draft reply for him to respond to Government. This was difficult to compose, because of the circumstances. T.S.L. had been incurring losses for a few years and in order to try to staunch the haemorrhage, it had recently undergone "restructuring" — a euphemism for cut-backs in both facilities and labour. The trouble was that, whatever the size of the company, it required sufficient volume of work to employ its labour and to recover at least part of its overheads. The dilemma was this — that by quoting a break-even price for each contract, the chances were high that it would secure no work, leading to large under-recovered overheads, not to mention the cost of labour on "idle time". By quoting well below break-even prices for each contract, the chances were high that sufficient work could be obtained to absorb all the labour and recover at least some of the overheads. By so doing of course, T.S.L. attracted the wrath of the private shiprepairers. So while the allegations contained in the S.S.I.A.'s letter were correct, so far as T.S.L. was concerned, the cost to the taxpayer was less if it managed to fill the place with work. Incidentally, most repair work involved "extras", which work had not formed part of the original repair specification and for which much higher prices could be levied.

Thus, despite the complaints of S.S.I.A., the T.S.L. strategy was correct in the circumstances in which they found themselves.

In the 3½ years I spent at Shiprepair, we never satisfactorily addressed this matter with Government. Of course the S.S.I.A. and its members were well aware of our strategy. After all they too were shiprepairers and were practising the same strategy. Their objective and I don't blame them, was to cite each instance of their failure to win contracts as unfair competition. This in the hope of persuading Government to force B.S. to quote each repair contract on a break-even basis, which would quickly cause the Repair Division to close. Then they could uplift their prices.

My office was part of T.S.L.'s offices at South Shields and this company was to absorb 75% of my time at Shiprepair. Despite the job losses that had occurred on a number of occasions, the shop stewards were pretty co-operative and the labour force worked harder than I had experienced in shipbuilding. There was a "No Strike Agreement" in force, which was strictly upheld. This arrangement was very helpful when marketing for shiprepair work in the U.K. and elsewhere. Unfortunately, the Board of T.S.L. did not pull together. The M.D. had been recently appointed and the Marketing Director had been his predecessor! These two did not share the same philosophy as the other three members of the Board insofar as the running of the company was concerned. One of the three others was transferred to a vacancy which occurred elsewhere in the Corporation and thereafter I frequently found myself as Chairman with the casting vote. But the Board was never harmonious.

T.S.L. had been awarded the refit of H.M.S. *Fearless*, sistership of H.M.S. *Intrepid*, of Clydebank fame. This work was in progress together with repair work on all manner of other ships, including Russian freighters. Rumour was rife that the reason why the Russian work was awarded to T.S.L. was because the Russians wanted to see what modifications were being carried out on H.M.S. *Fearless*. There may well have been a grain of truth in this, but T.S.L. had in any case repaired a number of Russian ships and were on reasonably good terms with their superintendent, who lived in Newcastle. But the "Special Branch" took no chances and this superintendent was only permitted to drive on one specified route from his home to South Shields and back. To what extent strict surveillance was practised I never knew, but I treated the guy with care.

Only a week or so after I moved to South Shields, we learned that C.T.C. Lines of London were calling for bids for the refit of an intermediate passenger liner. C.T.C. was a company that chartered Russian Liners for Worldwide cruising. Their Managing Director was a jovial Russian ex-captain from Vladivostok. His assistant was Eric Phippen, an equally pleasant chap. After completing the necessary design and estimating work and attending several meetings, a price was negotiated. We were advised that this price would probably be acceptable, but that the Technical Director of Black Sea Lines would arrive in London from Odessa to finalise the specification and the contract.

At this last meeting, we had to pare our price a little while the specification was being finalised. When we came to discuss the Force Majeure Clause in the contract, the Russian asked — "What is this 'Force Majeure'?". It was suggested to him that an Act of God constituted 'Force Majeure' for example. "Who is this God?" he wanted to know. We eventually got the job.

I visited the other three companies and met their Boards, senior staff and shop stewards. Grangemouth was a very small operation and I felt that it was in fairly capable hands. In any event, any losses that they might record were unlikely to rock the Division too much.

Falmouth was interesting. As a member of the Silley Cox

Shiprepairing Group and later P. & O., it had proved a handful. Strikes leading to late deliveries had plagued the company for years. Shortly after nationalisation, B.S. had been on the point of closing the company, but it was decided to give it one last chance. At one time, the company had employed over 1,000 people, but it was now down to a handful. The local management hammered out new pay deals and working practices and slowly started building up the company, choosing their employees with the greatest care. By the time I came on the scene, the numbers employed were around 400 and unbelievably the company had turned in trading profits of almost £1,000,000 in the last Financial Year. It was a brilliant success story. There were only three executive directors. I liked the Managing Director although he was sometimes a touch arrogant, but I felt he had reason to be! He personally worked extremely hard and clearly this outfit was in good hands.

The facilities of Vosper Shiprepairers at Southampton had at one time been owned by Harland & Wolff, in the palmy days when Southampton was the home port for the "Queens" and Union Castle Mail & Passenger Liners and was also the starting point for P. & O. cruises. These big ships were sailing to a strict schedule and so when repairs were required, the local shiprepairer obtained the work on a cost-plus basis. But that was 1961 and this was 1981. No longer did Union Castle exist. Only the *QE2* and P. & O.'s *Canberra* called at Southampton. There had been complaints from Cunard concerning unfinished work and allegations of unrealistic prices, in relation to the latest repairs undertaken on the *QE2*. Cunard threatened to send the vessel to either France or West Germany for future repair work. Clearly V.S.L. had not adjusted to the harsh climate now prevailing in shiprepair.

I met the two Board members and their staff, following which I met the shop stewards. At this first meeting, they proceeded to catalogue a list of complaints and demands. It was patently obvious that we were in for a rough ride here.

I have already mentioned that 75% of my time in shiprepair was taken up with T.S.L. affairs and I suppose another 20% was taken up by V.S.L.'s labour problems. But those percentages relate to the time spent, not only at the companies themselves, but also in meetings and reports on these companies with the Corporation.

Corporation Board Meetings, Divisional Board Meetings and

Company Board Meetings were held every other month. I was required to present a short report to the Corporation Board Meeting, be in attendance at the Shiprepair Divisional Board Meetings and chair the Board Meetings of the four shiprepair companies. Falmouth apart, the company Board Meetings were invariably concerned with losses being incurred and how to prevent them.

While the company Board Meetings were straightforward enough, the companies themselves were far apart geographically. To attend a T.S.L. Board Meeting I walked down the corridor! For Grangemouth Board Meetings I travelled up and down by train comfortably in a day. V.S.L. Board Meetings however involved a flight to London followed by the non-stop train journey from Waterloo to Southampton. The difficulty lay in getting to Falmouth from Southampton. In the winter, I returned to London and took the sleeper from Paddington to Truro and in the summer, I flew from Heathrow to Newquay the same evening. When I was really pushed, I sometimes convened the Falmouth Board Meeting in a hotel in Bath or Bristol, which saved me a good deal of time and hassle.

The Shiprepair Divisional Board Meetings were normally held at Benton House but sometimes in Knightsbridge. The Divisional Board consisted of the B.S. Chairman, the B.S. Board Member for Finance, myself, the Divisional Finance Director, the four Company Boards, the Divisional Marketing Director and any other persons the Chairman had instructed to attend the meeting for discussion of a particular topic. I had my first taste of a Divisional Board Meeting exactly one week after joining the Division.

Each subsidiary had provided a report on its full range of activities covering the previous eight weeks and the accumulated profit or loss from the beginning of the Financial Year was of course included. The Chairman opened the proceedings and immediately castigated the Division for its unacceptable financial performance. These meetings were always full of tension. Of course one could not defend the financial results, but there were other aspects of the Division's affairs where it became necessary to stand up for oneself.

The Shiprepair Division was the smallest division within the Corporation and as such, its Managing Director did not merit a place on the Main Corporation Board. I was required however to submit in advance of the Main Board Meeting a summary shiprepair report of no more than two pages. I then was instructed to report to the Board Room at Knightsbridge. Again, tension in the air.

After I had spent some time in Shiprepair the Chairman instigated "Performance Reviews" of all companies within the Corporation. These reviews entailed the Boards of each company being interrogated by a number of Corporation Board Members and senior officials and frequently lasted for several hours.

The Shiprepair Division carried a small marketing staff of three, all located at Knightsbridge. From time to time, they visited owners in the U.K. and abroad in an attempt to drum up business. In addition, the Division had appointed agents in various countries as far apart as the U.S.A. and India. The Corporation by this time had opened an office in Hong Kong and one of the staff there marketed on our behalf in both Hong Kong and mainland China. I was unhappy with the way in which we paid these agents and also with the performance of some of them.

The agents were paid a Retention Fee together with a Commission for any business which they introduced to the yards. I was not happy about paying a Retention Fee. I thought that a far better incentive would be — "no work — no fee". I wanted to meet all the agents but didn't fancy going on a World tour in order to do so and so arranged for them all to visit the U.K. More than a dozen turned up. I expressed the view that only a few of their number were regularly introducing business and that in general therefore, I wasn't satisfied with their performance as agents. When I then suggested the removal of the Retention Fee, uproar ensued. A modicum of order was restored when I proposed increasing the commission although it was clear that some of the agents would be happy not to renew their contracts with us. The three Norwegian and two Swedish agents were performing well enough and I took an instant liking to the Danish, Indian and Pakistan agents and resolved to visit them when I got the chance. I quickly came to the conclusion that our U.S.A. agent should be replaced, although he was one of those content with the new arrangements.

At the end of September I learned that the Delta Steamship Inc., of New Orleans was interested in lengthening and upgrading no less

than six of their 12,000 ton deadweight freighters. I asked our
U.S.A. agent in New York to find out the name of the President of
Delta and thereafter telex him requesting a meeting in New
Orleans. At 4.45 p.m. on a Friday, I received the following telex —
"Have Parker meet me at 7.30 a.m. for breakfast on the 12th floor
of the Downtown Hilton in New Orleans on Monday, signed A. E.
Gibson, President". I was there at the appointed time.

Then began a long series of negotiations that continued in New
York in October and in South Shields in November. Thereafter
Delta's attorney from Washington arrived in London for what
seemed an endless series of meetings concerning the terms of the
contract. These meetings continued at intervals until the following
Summer. Suddenly, just when the documentation was on the point
of completion, the deal was called off. Delta's parent, Holiday Inns
of Memphis, sold Delta Steamship Inc., to a shipping company in
California and these new owners were not interested in proceeding
further. Had the contract come off, it would have represented the
biggest piece of shiprepairing business seen in the U.K. for a very
long time. It was worth £41,000,000. It was as well that it didn't
happen, because if we had underestimated price and time on the
first vessel, then the loss incurred in both cost overruns and
penalties for lateness could be compounded by the further five
ships. Moreover, the U.S. attorney had forced some extremely tight
features into the contract.

At least I saw something of New Orleans, one of my favourite
places — the Gulf oysters, the Bourbon whisky, the French quarter,
the jazz, the Colonial houses with their slave-quarters, the
Mississippi and the Bayous. I asked someone in the hotel if
alligators still lurked in the river. He told me — "If you sit on the
goddam john too long Mac, you'll soon find out!".

V.S.L.'s labour problems continued apace and the matter simply
had to be tackled. Not that the problem was new to V.S.L. It was
clear that previous managements had turned their faces away from
confrontation. I was receiving a lot of stick from B.S. on account of
the Division's losses. While this was greatest at T.S.L., because it
was easily the largest company, the losses being recorded by V.S.L.
were worse on a pro-rata basis. I brought this matter to the
attention of the Chairman and the B.S. Industrial Relations
Director at every available opportunity. I wanted the Shipbuilding

Negotiating Committee (S.N.C.) of the Confederation to step into the fray, because the local union officials at Southampton seemed to me to be impotent.

At first, I could not persuade them of the seriousness of the problem. Months elapsed with more meetings to discuss the matter. Finally in July 1982, thirteen months after I had begun to alert B.S. to the problem, Jim Murray, General Secretary of the Boilermakers, agreed to personally "sort it out". I did not hear what he told the boilermaker stewards, because of course he didn't want to wash this particular piece of dirty linen in front of us. But when he emerged from his "discussions", he looked very red in the face. The stewards were ashen-faced.

The problems were two-fold. First, all trades exhibited an unbelievably low productivity. Second, the boilermakers had resisted all efforts to persuade them to undertake flexibility and interchangeability between trades, something which had been common practice across the industry for a decade or more. Hence, when the *QE2* arrived for her annual refit, platers refused point blank to interchange with shipwrights and vice-versa. During the course of the work, there was say, a demand for shipwrights but not for platers. The only recourse under the circumstances, was either to recruit shipwrights from "off the streets", who were in any case practically unemployable or not recruit, in which case the contract ran late. Meanwhile and this was the rub, the platers for whom there was no work, were sent home on "idle time". It was suspected that a number of them had taxi hire businesses! Jim Murray improved the situation with his boilermakers. The low productivity remained a problem.

I flew to Hong Kong at the end of November 1981 in company with the Divisional Marketing Director. Newton Cheng, the man in our Hong Kong office designated to market for shiprepair in the Colony as well as China, met us at the airport. Unfortunately, the Cathay Pacific Boeing 747 from Gatwick had developed engine trouble an hour after leaving Bahrain and we had to turn back. A delay of 24 hours resulted. I was very upset at this development since I had only allowed myself seven days away from the U.K. and I had not bargained on spending one full day lazing around the Bahrain Hilton Hotel swimming pool.

Newton Cheng had set up meetings with a large number of

Chinese shipowners and these we visited in turn. All were excessively polite, but all expressed concern at the refusal of our labour forces to permit ship's crews undertaking minor repairs while their ships were on our premises. Although some opposition to this fast-growing practice had been encountered, this was all in the past. It illustrates once again how long it takes to win a good reputation and how short a time it can take to lose it.

I was fascinated by Hong Kong and the view from Kowloon across to the island at night was a truly wonderful sight. The Mandarin Hotel at Hong Kong ensured that our stay was very pleasant. I wasn't too keen on the Chinese food, especially when nearing the end of a fish course forming part of the lunch we were hosting for some Chinese owners, Newton Cheng suddenly said — "Mr. Parker, the fish's head is pointing to you — it is yours!". The baleful eyes of this once-proud denizen of the deep quite put me off!

British Shipbuilders gave regular presentations to the S.N.C. on the State of the Industry. For this, each Divisional Director was required to make a presentation on behalf of his Division. This required a big input and the graphs, indicating the market, prices and other data were projected on an overhead screen. There was a full dress rehearsal of this presentation some week or so before the event.

My first experience of such a presentation was in January 1982 and by this time the Conservative Government had began to tame the unions across most industries. As I listened to each present-ation, for the first time I began to feel sorry for the union officials. They were presented with nothing but bad news — falling markets, falling prices, increasing losses in all Divisions, except of course for the Naval Division. The implications were first redundancies and later, closures and more redundancies.

By the Spring of 1982, shiprepair losses had not abated. The market was even worse. A decision to restructure T.S.L. yet again, was taken. A series of meetings were held at both Benton House and Knightsbridge to draw together the likely numbers involved and the extent of facilities to be retained. When this had been finalised, a presentation had to be made to the S.N.C. This was followed by explanations to South Shields Council in their Chambers. Unemployment was already high in South Shields and here we were going to increase it for the second time in 18 months.

In the Spring also, company budgets were in the course of being finalised in readiness for their inclusion in the Corporate plan. I was involved now with five separate budgets — one for each company and one for my own small H.Q. Once finalised in-house, they were then reviewed and amended at Benton House in a series of further meetings.

Around this time I reflected upon my current duties and what they involved. A study of my diaries reveals meetings with British Shipbuilders H.Q. personnel virtually every week and frequently several times in a week, on budgets, Corporate Plan, union presentations, presentations to Ministers, salary reviews, shiprepair strategy, restructuring proposals and industrial relations problems, each of these involving paperwork. Every other month of course, I was involved in four company Board Meetings and Divisional and Main Board Meetings — involving more paperwork.

I wasn't enjoying the work for a number of reasons. First, I was no longer a Chief Executive of one company — a "line manager" and I missed that kind of existence where at least one had a lot less contact with H.Q. Second, everything about shiprepair appeared to be "bad news". I personally was extremely sorry for the staff and workforce of T.S.L., who were truly a hard-working bunch, yet they had to suffer all this pain of redundancy after redundancy. Third of course, I missed shipbuilding.

My only means of relief from all these "talking shops" and reports was to lead teams abroad to follow up enquiries for conversion work. Prior to my joining the Repair Division, it had not been established to what extent, if any, credit facilities were available for conversion work. I was aware that such facilities were not available for run-of-the-mill jobs costing anything up to £400,000. In discussions with the Export Credit Guarantee Department, I discovered that in fact credit was available for conversion work costing in excess of this figure. From that point onwards I took a close interest in all conversion contracts.

At the beginning of 1982, T.S.L. had responded to an enquiry from the Shipping Corporation of India for the conversion of a very elderly small vessel into a geological survey vessel. By February they had submitted a price and specification to Bombay. I kept in touch with our agent there, to ensure that he was getting feed-back from the owners about the competition and how the owners had reacted to our offer. I told him that I was prepared to negotiate on the price and then, once the price was agreed and we knew the job was ours, we would fly out to Bombay to finalise the specification and contract. Eventually the price was agreed and I duly presented our small team to the owners in their offices in Bombay.

After a number of pleasantries had been exchanged in the most civilised manner possible, the owner's spokesman calmly announced that our price was too high! I immediately rose to my feet, followed by our team and advised the owners that we would take the first flight out of Bombay for London. Our agent was dumbfounded! He had quite a job to persuade us to stay. We agreed to do so but only if both sides for the moment confined the discussions to the specification and the contract and we could revert to the price when this stage has been reached. I hoped that by so doing, the changes I thought the owners would probably make to the specification would justify a new price anyhow. This turned out to be the case and in due course the contract was signed.

At the end of May 1982 I visited our Danish agent in Copenhagen and met a number of shipowners. One of these contacts was to lead to repair work in the following year. I flew on to Oslo and met two more of our agents and was again introduced to a large number of shipowners. I couldn't help noticing the fine lifestyle that these agents enjoyed. All three owned largish yachts. I went for two trips "round the bay" and each time was royally entertained.

Talking of yachts, in July 1982, The Tall Ships Race started at Falmouth. All the craft taking part were moored alongside the jetties of F.S.L. and a fine sight they were. There was a huge firework display on the night before the race and cocktail parties were taking place onboard a number of vessels. The Managing Director of F.S.L. had organised that my wife and I, together with him and his wife, would be guests aboard the frigate H.M.S. *Londonderry* for the start of the race. The Duke of Edinburgh personally fired the starting gun. Everything that could float had turned out to see the Armada depart. It became impossible to distinguish the boats that were racing from those that were following. How collisions were avoided I will never know. It was a truly magnificent sight.

In response to our Pakistan agent, two of us flew out to Karachi in October 1982. Basically there were only two shipowners in Pakistan. One was the Pakistan National Shipping Line and the other wasn't! The one that wasn't was the Pan-Islamic Shipping Company, a small outfit that operated pilgrim ships. They were interested in buying a second-hand SD14 standard cargoship and having it converted to carry pilgrims. Discussions began in their sparse offices with their Chairman and two other staff. A few minutes later, a fourth member appeared and was introduced as the Marine Superintendent. He turned to me with a broad grin and said — "George, I'm delighted to see you after such a long time!". I'm afraid his name conveyed nothing to me. In fact, he had been the second officer on the *Saudi*, the Lithgow-built pilgrim vessel completed 26 years previously!

The discussions led to much technical work being undertaken by T.S.L. in subsequent months, but as is so often the case, the Pan-Islamic Co., had not the financial muscle to carry through a project of this size, although this was not immediately evident. Pan-Islamic's Chairman claimed to be a personal friend of the then President of Pakistan and believed that he would be given Government financial backing for this project. This was not forthcoming.

Our Pakistan agent introduced me to his friends at Pakistan National Shipping Line. My colleagues already knew them, for T.S.L. had undertaken a number of repairs to that company's ships. Each night we ended up at our agent's house and were served the most delicious Indian (and Pakistani) meals. Despite the Moslem ban on the drinking of alcohol, whisky was consumed before, during and after the meals!

After that first meeting with Pan-Islamic, I flew home via Athens. Our agents in Pireaus were one of our oldest and from time to time, introduced us to repair work. We called on a number of shipowners. I thought it courteous to call on the newly-opened Corporation office some short distance from our agent's office. The newly-appointed manager left me in no doubt that he considered that he should be looking after all the Corporation's interests in Greece, including shiprepair. He was a little less than compliment-ary concerning our agent's activities. It was immediately evident that each hated the other's guts. I thought at the time that it wasn't too bright of the Corporation to set up this office and ignore our agent in the process. Nor did I think that this acrimonious situation would promote a good image for the Corporation in Greece. Since I was quite satisfied with this agent's performance, I let the matter pass.

By the Spring of 1983, we had not received a single enquiry through our U.S.A. agent and it was decided to replace him. Taking one of the shiprepair marketing team with me, we flew to New York where we interviewed a number of candidates. I didn't think too much of any of them. We did the same in New Orleans and I liked the people there even less. In the end, we appointed one of those interviewed in New York because of his long history in the U.S. shipbuilding industry and his apparent comprehensive knowledge of U.S. shipowners. There was however, one thing that I didn't like about him. He was quite unable to explain how the U.S. Differential Building Subsidy and Differential Operating Subsidy worked in practice. I was vaguely aware that one or other or both, were paid on condition that U.S. owners did not order new ships or conversions, abroad. I was also vaguely aware that the conditions were likely to be relaxed. Anyway our new man could not enlighten me.

Throughout the previous year, V.S.L. had been having discussions in London with a well known firm of interior designers who had been commissioned to design the interior of a large and luxurious yacht for the King of Saudi Arabia. One thing V.S.L. was good at was high-class joiner work and they were very interested in trying to secure the contract for the Royal suites and public rooms. The vessel had been built and partially fitted out in Scandinavia. The interior designers had been authorised to select the company who would give effect to their joinery designs. They favoured V.S.L. and eventually the contract was placed and the vessel arrived at Southampton. The ship was complete in every respect except for the joiner work mentioned. In the Royal suites and public rooms, all wiring, plumbing and ventilation had been completed. The contract price was a little in excess of £9,000,000 — just for this joiner work! I never saw the *Abdul Aziz* completed, but understand that the Royal toilet walls were tiled in lapis lazuli, especially selected from Afghanistan.

The vessels forming the Royal Fleet Auxiliary were refitted at both Royal Dockyards and commercial shiprepairers. It was generally accepted that the Royal Dockyard's prices were very high in comparison to commercial shiprepairers. Nevertheless, R.F.A. vessels were regularly repaired at the Dockyards and no doubt this was naval policy. But when an R.F.A. vessel was out to "open" tender, the competition was intense. But usually such work yielded lots of extras for which much higher prices could be levied and thus any shortfall in the original contract price could be recovered. The Shiprepair Division had undergone a number of changes since its stewardship by British Shipbuilders. Moreover, work was still in short supply, particularly at T.S.L. and so I decided to do a little public relations with the Royal Fleet Auxiliary.

In May 1983, we gave a Shiprepair Presentation to the Admiral Fleet Support (I.C. of Royal Dockyards), Director General Ships Staff from Bath together with the Head of the R.F.A. and his Staff. It went off pretty well and although it failed in its objective of securing more R.F.A. business, it opened up a new avenue for work.

The R.M.A.S. was based at Bath and was responsible for no less than 600 small craft — barges, lighters, tugs, craneships and the like. The boss of this section attended our presentation. He introduced himself and suggested I come to his office in Bath for a discussion. I did so the following month and received a really warm welcome. He first of all stated that I was the first commercial shiprepairer that he had ever met and that he approved of our aim in trying to secure more work at the expense of the Royal Dockyards. He considered that the Dockyards treated the R.M.A.S. badly and instanced numerous occasions where R.N. and R.F.A. vessels were given priority. He had vessels lying at all four Dockyards doing nothing. Accordingly, he welcomed the possibility of having us undertake some of his repair work. I stayed long enough in the Repair Division to see the beginning of this process, but regretted very much not having woken up to this possibility three years earlier.

British Shipbuilders were keen to privatise the repair yards and favoured management buy-outs. G.D.L., T.S.L. and V.S.L. managements were all approached. V.S.L. management said they would think about it and revert. Apart from V.S.L. the companys' managements immediately welcomed the idea and the Corporation encouraged them to start working up a Business Plan. Then a strange thing happened at T.S.L. I have already referred to the division within the T.S.L. Board. This rift once again surfaced in the shape of rival management bids for the company!

The Chairman's three year appointment was completed in the Summer of 1983 and he then retired (and was later knighted). He was succeeded by Graham Day.

Later in the year, arrangements were completed for the management buy-out of both G.D.L. and T.S.L. — in the latter case of course, there were both winners and losers. V.S.L. management were now said to be preparing a Business Plan, in readiness for a buy-out.

Suddenly on the 14th December 1983, I was called to the Chairman's office at Knightsbridge and offered the job of Managing Director of Austin & Pickersgill in Sunderland, with effect from 3rd January 1984. I had no idea what shocks awaited me, but I was more than delighted to be returning to shipbuilding.

CHAPTER 18

AUSTIN & PICKERSGILL LIMITED

AUSTIN & PICKERSGILL (A & P) at Southwick on the North Bank of the River Wear was, without doubt, one of the most modern shipyards in Europe. The yard had not been modernised so much as almost completely rebuilt. This work was completed a little time before the industry was nationalised in 1977. The new yard was laid out for series production of standard cargo ships and bulk carriers up to around 35,000 tons deadweight.

The steelwork facilities in particular, were quite first-class. The plate and section preparation shops were equipped with the most modern and sophisticated plant for handling batch production, with roller conveyors much in evidence. An equally impressive fabrication shop lay immediately adjacent to the preparation sheds.

Some distance away, at the far end of the yard was the "Building Complex". This comprised a completely enclosed facility for building ships under cover. It basically consisted of two long bays, one being a conventional slipway served by three 60-tons overhead travelling cranes. The adjacent bay was stepped, one third of the way up from the river end. The lower portion was also a slipway where stern sections of ships were constructed. Raised above this part-slipway was a level area where fabricated units were joined into larger units prior to being erected on one or other of the berths. Three 60-tons overhead travelling cranes covered both part-slipway and fabrication area.

The engine rooms and accommodation areas of modern bulk carriers and cargo vessels are located near the stern and this most complex part of the ship accordingly determines the build-cycle time. The layout described allowed hull construction to commence at the stern end of one vessel while its predecessor was building simultaneously on the complete berth. When the first vessel was launched, the stern section of the second vessel was jacked hydraulically into position on the vacated berth and the cycle repeated.

A modern and modest sized office block housed the majority of the staff, including the Technical Department. This department was small in numbers, but it had to be borne in mind that for the period of more than two decades, A & P had completed no less than 125 of their famous standard cargo ships — the SD14 — meaning "standard deadweight 14,000 tons". The yard had subsequently developed three standard bulk carriers — the B26, the B30 and the B35. Thus a large Technical Department would have been surplus to requirements.

Up until a few years prior to 1984, A & P had consistently made very good profits and were unquestionably one of the jewels of the U.K. shipbuilding industry. This was achieved despite very high wage levels and overhead costs, because of the high throughput of ships. But things had changed. Despite updating the SD14 on a number of occasions, this design had run its course and other more modern cargo ship designs had superseded it. In any case, the freight market had all but collapsed. Modern bulk carriers for example, could not command charter rates that would cover anything like their operating, maintenance and depreciation costs.

Hence it came about that in January 1984, A & P had a very poor order book. This consisted of one and as it turned out the last SD14, three B30 bulk carriers, one B35 bulk carrier and two cargo vessels for the Ethiopian National Line. The problem was that the three B30 vessels were all on the point of completion and their Greek owner had refused to take delivery, while construction of the B35 vessel had been "put on ice" by its Hong Kong owner. The SD14 was also nearing completion. So, to all intents and purposes, only two Ethiopian ships were under construction with no further contracts in prospect. This was the order book that I inherited.

Before taking up my duties, I was advised that changes were to take place in the A & P Board. A little later, the Corporation advised the names of those who would, over the next three of four months, form the new Board. No consultation was thought necessary in arriving at this list of names.

I met the Board and management, but the shop stewards refused to see me! The threat of a national strike loomed over the industry at the time and feelings were running high. Contingency plans had been drawn up to cope with an expected "yard occupation" by the labour force and the local police had been consulted.

In the end, all this was averted and I duly met the stewards about 10 days later. I was much impressed with their obvious power and apparent distrust of management.

How the mighty had fallen! I had never seen such a contractual, production and labour relations shambles in shipbuilding. For a start, the three B30 bulk carriers moored at the outfit jetty, could not be handed over to their owner because he had alleged that, like the first vessel already in service, they suffered from extensive welding cracks to their main structure. What was worse was that there appeared to be no company strategy for dealing with this serious and urgent matter.

Secondly, the B35 bulk carrier, whose construction had been frozen, had reached a stage in building where the stern section of the vessel, including the superstructure, was fully built in the "complex". The rest of the vessel's fabrication was complete and 75 or so prefabricated units were lying all over the shipyard! There was no strategy for dealing with this major problem either!

The first Ethiopian ship was half-built on the full berth in the complex and was to be followed by the sister vessel. Until the second vessel was launched, the stern section of the B35 was locked in .

Since there were only two Ethiopian ships under construction, the yard's labour force, particularly steelworkers, were nothing like fully employed. All this idle time was being clocked up against the B35 and the Ethiopian ships, thus totally distorting the true labour costs involved. Again, there was no management plan for dealing with this.

It was clear that industrial relations were strained and that productivity was low due partly no doubt to the shortage of work.

These crucial issues besetting the company may have been addressed by individual Board Members, but at any rate they remained totally unresolved and it was imperative that they be tackled at once.

I considered that of all the problems facing A & P, none was more urgent than that of obtaining more work. This would provide a breathing space for sorting out all the other matters. The trouble was — shortage of time. The first Ethiopian ship was three-quarters built with only the sister vessel to follow. Our Technical Department was, as I have already mentioned, comparatively lightweight.

Ideally what we needed urgently was steelwork but steelwork that required a minimum of design work and Drawing Office development. The answer seemed to be flat-topped barges. Only a few months previously T.S.L. had tendered for the construction of a number of barges which, when connected together, could form a loading and discharge facility for Port Stanley in the Falkland Islands. In the process of tendering, we met barge owners. Less than two weeks after joining A & P I happened to meet the head of this company at a Shipwrights' dinner in London. I gave him the gist of our difficulty and suggested that, if I could get permission from the Corporation to build a barge at less than cost, would he be interested? After that, events moved swiftly.

The Corporation confirmed, after consultation with the D.T.I., that an ocean-going non-propelled barge could attract Intervention Fund subsidy. After further discussions the D.T.I., confirmed with the greatest reluctance, that we could quote at less than a break-even price and still apply for the subsidy. The proviso was that this work did not extend our order book but was merely filling a gap in our programme. Their logic was sound. They reasoned that if we were not to fill in the programme gap, our existing overheads would be incurred in any case. On this basis, we signed a contract for a 300 foot North Sea barge on the 30th March 1984 with an option on a second unit.

At a meeting convened between the Corporation and the S.N.C. at the time of the T.U.C. Conference at Blackpool some years before, it had been established that the Corporation could never implement compulsory redundancies. Because of this so-called "Blackpool Agreement", a number of merchant shipbuilding yards and repair yards were unable to release employees for whom there was no work. This was the situation at A & P. It cost the Corporation and the tax payer a fortune over the years.

I was determined to segregate those for whom there was no work from the rest, in order that only working hours were charged against contracts. Thus began a quite ludicrous period in which sizeable numbers of boilermakers were "cabined up" in various canteens during the working day, while their mates were going about their normal business. Hardly a recipe for increased productivity! We tried to enlist the support of the shop stewards in calling for voluntary redundancies but with little success. This situation continued until we were able to start work on further contracts.

The allegations of extensive cracking of main structural welding on four bulk carriers was of course of major concern. In early February, the matter was discussed with Lloyd's Register in London, following which each of the remaining three vessels lying at our outfit jetty were thoroughly examined by Lloyds and reports made available. The allegations were correct!

As has already been mentioned, the bulk carrier market had collapsed and there was no doubt in my mind that the Greek owner no longer wanted these ships, at least for the time being, since they would only result in operational losses. We had already given him a ready-made reason for refusing to accept delivery. Contractually however, provided the ships were issued with Lloyd's Interim Certificates, the owner would have to accept delivery. This involved of course repairing the very extensive defects not just on the three vessels yet to deliver. but on the other vessel already in service.

In mid-March 1984, I decided to get all the parties concerned to a meeting in London. There were many and various and included the owner and his technical staff, his London solicitor, Williams & Glyn's Bank (the lending bank), E.C.G.D. (the guarantor), our in-house lawyer and finally A & P staff. This meeting was the first of many.

Ultimately, the finance package for all four ships was restructured to provide some relief to the shipowner. In this process both E.C.G.D. and A & P agreed to financial concessions. The bank, with whom the owner had a large dollar sum on deposit by way of guarantee for the loan advance, agreed to revalue the loan in terms of sterling. They were able to do this because the dollar had greatly strengthened against sterling. That part of the deposit no longer required as a bank guarantee would be used to pay A & P the final instalment outstanding on all three vessels. Quite a performance! Meanwhile arrangements were made to carry out the extensive repairs necessary to the welding defects and this was a very expensive exercise. The last of these vessels was handed over in August 1984.

Meanwhile events had taken place in relation to the B35 bulk carrier whose construction had been frozen. I was verbally advised by a senior official of the Corporation H.Q. staff that this contract was now cancelled. This meant that A & P was left with a partly built ship and no owner to finance the remaining construction.

I immediately sought permission to restart building the ship with a view to finding an owner before delivery. This was agreed to and soon afterwards a recently retired Lloyd's Surveyor was appointed to act in the capacity of an owner's inspector for the purpose of supervising the remaining construction. I have already described how the stern section of this ship was completely built but was locked into the "stern" building berth. It could not be jacked across to the main building berth until the launch of the Second Ethiopian vessel. This launch was not scheduled until October and of course the yard badly needed steelwork. Thus it was decided to build the main part of the vessel "bow first" on an open slipway. After launching the intention was for this section of the vessel to be towed to a Tyne drydock and there joined up with the stern section to be launched in late October.

Thus by April 1984, the contractual shambles in relation to the four B30 bulk carriers had been resolved, albeit at a price. We had an order for a steel barge on which some of the technical department were occupied and which would shortly provide a little work for boilermakers. Moreover we could immediately employ most if not all of our surplus boilermakers on the berth work of the B35. This was progress!

Egon Oldendorff, a West German shipowner, located in Lübeck, had taken delivery of a number of SD14s from A & P and was now in the market for two multi-purpose cargo vessels of around 21,000 tons deadweight. The enquiry had been received in the last quarter of 1983 and we submitted our price and specification in February 1984. Later that same month we discussed this submission with the owners in Lübeck. There we learned of many changes to the specification which required us to go back to the drawing board. At the same time we were advised that the competition was international, including Brazil and Yugoslavia.

We submitted our new price and specification in early June and in the middle of that month were called back to Lübeck. The B.S. Chairman elected to join us. It soon became clear that our price was way above the competition, even when assisted by subsidy. I was pretty sure the project, so far as we were concerned, was dead. I was to be proved wrong.

Although the very short-term lack of steelwork had been cured, the yard badly needed another ship order. I had met the general manager of the Ethiopian National Shipping Line in his Rotterdam office on a couple of occasions and he encouraged me to submit a price to his head office in Addis Ababa for two more ships, similar to those we were building. Three of us flew out to Addis Ababa in early July for discussions with owners and government officials. We were very well received but the news was not encouraging for two reasons. First, then as now, there were a number of different wars taking place on or close to Ethiopian soil. The President of Ethiopia was a Communist and was receiving Russian military aid. Second, the Italians had quoted for repeat vessels and their government had offered a package including the ships, together with a list of other goods manufactured in Italy on the most unbelievably favourable credit terms. I recall these being 15 years at a fixed interest rate of 2½%! This compared with the standard U.K. credit terms for ships which was 80% of the price repayable over seven years at a fixed interest rate of 7½%.

Many months were to elapse before I finally admitted defeat with this project. Basically what killed our chances was the fact that E.C.G.D. were very reluctant to guarantee any more credit to Ethiopia, for two reasons. First, they were considered a high-risk so far as repayment of any loans were concerned and second, because their State coffers had been badly dented by the purchase of two 767 Boeing jets, not to mention the continuing drain on financial resources caused by the purchase of military equipment.

A & P meanwhile had launched the first Ethiopian vessel in May. At the reception following the launch, I accepted on behalf of the company a gift from the owners. Conservationists please take note. It was a pair of Ethiopian elephant tusks in a presentation case. I privately felt afterwards that we ought to grind them down and distribute the powder to our labour force. It might have improved their productivity! (*See illustrations*).

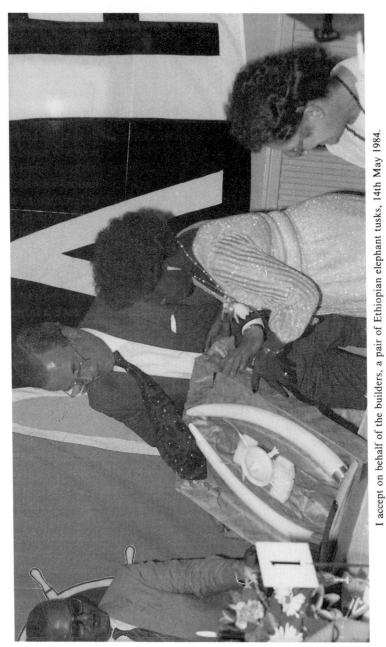

I accept on behalf of the builders, a pair of Ethiopian elephant tusks, 14th May 1984.

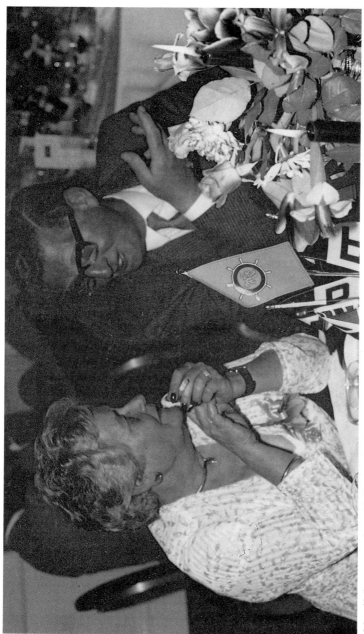

My wife in conversation with Gordon Bagier, MP at the reception following the launch of the first of two cargo vessels for the Ethiopian National Shipping Line, 14th May 1984.

The first half of 1984 passed in a flash. There had been a lot of problems to tackle and I had been extremely busy coping with these. As usual however, the Corporation's Headquarters was continuing to make progress in its unreal world. Meetings were called at H.Q. on a variety of different topics — Product Development, Rationalisation of Shipyard Facilities, Sales Task Forces as well as the usual quota of meetings on Budgets and Corporate Plan. Leaving Sunderland and arriving at Benton House was akin to leaving the cold winds of the shipbuilding world and entering the sanctuary of a heated greenhouse. At this point the Corporation decided to employ consultants who would apparently make available to us their expertise in "team building and problem solving". This required the Managing Directors of the merchant yards, large and small, to attend weekend seminars at country hotels. I treated these seminars privately as a rest from my labours.

In May 1984, Cooper & Lybrand, the Accountants, gave us a presentation on "Priority Based Budgeting". This was their method of reducing company overheads by applying certain principles. It appealed to me for two reasons — first, because I was aware that our overheads were too high and second, the methodology involved our own staff and not outside consultants reviewing the overheads. By July, we had decided to implement the proposals. The process was completed some nine months later and was a resounding success.

Throughout the rest of 1984, efforts were made on our behalf by London brokers to find a buyer for our B35 now rapidly taking shape on the berth. Mexicans and Greeks showed an interest but neither was brought to finality.

On 24th October, the second Ethiopian ship was launched (*See illustration*) and immediately thereafter, the stern section of the B35 was jacked across to take its place and launched soon afterwards.

The barge was laid down on the berth vacated in the complex and some seven weeks later was launched complete. On 17th December, following the launch reception, the owners took delivery, paid us the final instalment of the price and sold the barge there and then to French owners. Then they took up their option with us for a second barge. Thus ended a hectic first year for me at A & P.

By late 1984, our review of company overheads using Priority Based Budgeting techniques, had thrown up a number of staff

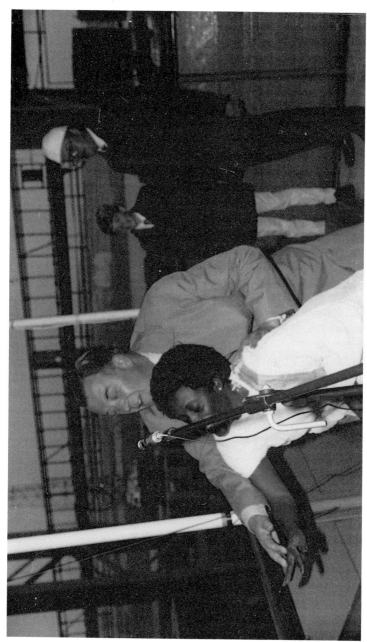

"Lets both push the boat out". Launch of the second Ethiopian cargo vessel, 24th October 1984.

surpluses, together with the financial advantages to be gained by sub-contracting electrical work, blacksmith work and staging work. Financial benefits would also be gained by combining painters with redleaders. These conclusions if implemented, implied hourly paid redundancies, in addition to staff redundancies. The effect of the savings, if fully implemented, would reduce our overhead cost from 208% of direct labour costs to 140% of direct labour costs. Although the unions continued to maintain that there could be no question of compulsory redundancies, we were confident that over a period of months we could achieve the reductions by voluntary means. Accordingly, for future tendering purposes, we intended to apply the proposed new overhead rate.

Firefighting but not new orders had characterised 1984. The year had only brought orders for two North Sea barges and the first had already been delivered. The first Ethiopian ship had been delivered towards the end of the year and the second vessel had been launched. The main section of the B35 was approaching launch stage on the outside berth. So, unless we could win ship orders very soon, I could see closure staring us in the face. Our failure to persuade E.C.G.D. to support Ethiopia for more vessels had been a heavy blow.

Oldendorff however, had still not placed contracts for his proposed cargo vessels and our broker encouraged us to resubmit a price now that the dollar had strengthened against sterling. This fact alone would make our price more competitive. It was known that the Brazilians had quoted in dollars and of course Oldendorff's shipping earnings were also in dollars and so the exchange rate was critical for us.

Before requoting however, the shop stewards were appraised of the crucial nature of this possible business. They were accordingly asked to accept the overhead reductions leading to job losses and were also appraised of the imperative need to raise their productivity.

In early January 1985, we resumed discussions with Oldendorff in Lübeck. There we learned that our revised price, improved by exchange rate movements and by lower future overheads and by an assumed increase in productivity, was much more competitive. It was stated to be still higher than Yugoslavia. The Brazilians had been discarded, presumably on account of the strengthened dollar.

I suggested to Henning Oldendorff that he should travel to London in the near future for a meeting with our Chairman, if I could arrange this. Three weeks later this meeting took place.

Meantime our tender price was placed under the microscope by Corporation officials. The productivity and overhead assumptions were discussed at length. As usual, the basis on which a subsidy could be given, was a break-even price.

The meeting took place on 25th January in Knightsbridge with the Chairman present. Henning Oldendorff spelled out the Yugoslav price and much discussion ensued. The meeting was inconclusive and it was agreed to meet again in six days time for the purpose of giving the Corporation and A & P more time to see if there was any way in which they could close the price gap.

Early the following week I advised the shop stewards of the outcome of these discussions. In particular, if the meeting scheduled for the following Thursday did not result in a contract signature then in my opinion, A & P would close.

Before this final meeting took place however, I came under the most intense pressure from the Chairman, Finance and Industrial Relations Directors, who all it seemed, were quite unwilling to accept that we could achieve the overhead reductions that we had built into the tender price. The pressure from all three was unremitting and lasted all day. Every detail of our reductions was questioned. Everyone knew, although it was left unsaid, that failure to win this business meant "curtains". At the end of a very heavy day, I thought we had convinced them.

At the last moment, the final meeting scheduled for Thursday, was postponed by 24 hours. It took place in the Board Room at Knightsbridge on 1st February, with Graham Day in the chair. He conducted the most skilful negotiation with Henning Oldendorff and although the price had to be reduced, it was still above what the Yugoslavs were stated to have quoted. The revised price was accepted and this whole process had taken some two hours. Everyone stood up and shook hands. I was hugely relieved.

Immediately afterwards a hiccup occurred when it was suggested that the ships might be built at Sunderland Shipbuilders, who because of their lower wage rates, could better match the price now agreed. Henning Oldendorff prevailed upon the Corporation to allow the ships to be built at A & P where a number of his earlier ships had been built.

It was at this point that one of the Corporation staff at Knightsbridge advised me that all A & P's hourly paid labour force had walked out on strike from starting time that morning. I also learned that this action had been taken apparently in protest against the failure to announce contracts the previous day — the original date of the final meeting. What a big help this was!

I was then called into the Chairman's office. He was alone. I was informed in no uncertain terms that if A & P were to build these ships, he required the stewards' signatures to an agreement which covered acceptance of our overhead reduction proposals, together with a guarantee that the boilermakers would build the vessels at the level of productivity built into the revised price. He advised me that since the owner was leaving Knightsbridge at noon the next day (Saturday), I had until 11.00 a.m. to secure such an agreement. Once secured I was to fax it to Knightsbridge where his officials, together with the owner would be awaiting its arrival. He was fully aware that our entire labour force was on strike. The time was now 4.00 p.m. — I had 19 hours!

The shop stewards were contacted in clubs and pubs and by telegram at home. The full committee were in attendance by 9.00 a.m. the following day. By 10.30 a.m. we had thrashed out an agreement and by 11.00 a.m. it was typed, signed and faxed to Knightsbridge. B.S. thereafter confirmed that A & P would build the ships. We celebrated this event in the A & P Board Room until well into the afternoon.

When I returned home, I reflected upon events over recent months. There was no doubt now in my mind that the Corporation had intended to close the yard. This aim had been thwarted. In short, we had saved the yard, for the time being at least. The A & P Board was now working really well together and they were a source of great strength to me. But the shop stewards remained a problem. They had opposed most of our efforts over the past year to get them to accept any changes. I privately did not believe that they could "deliver the goods" contained in the agreement just signed. They gave no hint that they were pleased that the yard had been saved. I think they took it as a matter of course.

I realised also that I was becoming more and more disenchanted with the Corporation's policies and in particular with their arms' length relationship with subsidiaries. Their officials were obsessed with productivity schemes, rationalisation of facilities, project management and a host of other subjects, all no doubt of some importance. I was obsessed with survival. I didn't doubt that I was unpopular at H.Q. and I spent as little time as possible at either office. Knightsbridge in particular made me "see red". After nearly eight years of nationalisation, not one single piece of business had emanated from the Corporation's marketing staff, so far as I was concerned. And this despite the Corporation's obsession with productivity and excessive overheads!

Later in February, a few of us flew out to Athens to follow up a Greek shipowner's possible interest in purchasing our B35. George Dracopolous was an old customer of A & P and was well pleased with his SD14s. We had met him in London late the previous year, since when he had his inspectors survey the ship and make a report. We spent nearly three days discussing the matter but the business was not concluded.

Smit Internationale B.V., of Rotterdam, had purchased the second North Sea barge, which was now under construction in the shipbuilding complex. In February, we quoted Smit for a further unit and in early March discussed the matter further in Rotterdam. Ernst Vossenar, a thoroughly agreeable man, signed the contract there and then. On 20th March, barge number 2 was launched and delivered a few days later to Smit.

About this time also we were in discussion with Knight's of Rochester for barge number 4. Shortly afterwards a contract was signed. The workload position now was — two North Sea barges and two 21,000-ton deadweight multi-purpose cargo vessels. The B35 hull sections had been joined together and the vessel was outfitting afloat.

I decided that the time had come for me to see a little of Japanese shipbuilding. Encouraged by the Corporation, A & P had entered into a Technical Agreement with Mitsubishi and part of this Agreement allowed us access to their production methods. A few of our staff had already visited their Shimonoseki shipyard, a yard of roughly similar size to A & P. I was joined on the trip by the Managing Director of Sunderland Shipbuilders. As usual, I arranged to be away for too short a period — seven days including flying time!

It was a thoroughly interesting trip. Their shipyard was certainly not as well equipped as our own, yet was producing a prodigious output of dissimilar ships. The key to this of course was their high productivity. No-one "broke sweat" but no-one stopped working. On my return I told our shop stewards that I was seriously thinking of introducing a novel feature into our day-to-day operations at Southwick. It was called a "work-break" — that is, a period of time during each day when work would be performed!

The highlight of the Japanese trip for me was our last evening in Shimoneseki. The two of us were invited to join shipyard executives for dinner in the company guest house. This was a fine large house built in traditional Japanese style and set in large gardens. Our hosts were all standing in a line on the long front doorstep waiting to greet us. They wore slippers. There were two spare pairs for us. We toured the house and before entering the dining room, removed our slippers.

Eight places were set at the low table — six on the one side and two on the other. I think they wanted see our faces when we ate the sea-slugs! The dining table was just high enough to get my legs under, sitting on an upholstered chair with no legs. Our hosts had taken the trouble to translate the menu into English. This was unfortunate, not only because of its contents, but also because it ran to nine courses! We were provided with an elderly geisha girl each, whose sole duty appeared to be confined to topping up our porcelain cup of warm saki. We ate with chopsticks and without anything other than minor mishaps.

After a number of cupfuls of saki had been despatched and about half way through the meal, the Japanese General Manager asked what I thought of the saki. I told him that I quite liked it but would have preferred it a little stronger. The geishas disappeared and returned with eight tumblers of liquid, one of which they placed in front of each member of the party. Floating on top of this colourless liquid was an object that closely resembled a bumble-bee. I waited and watched, but thought the worst! Using chopsticks the Japanese removed the objects and toasted us. This was delicious stuff! It was explained that this was high-class saki, flavoured by the fin of a poisonous fish — hence the black and gold object. I remember thinking that if I was going to be poisoned, then this was a pretty pleasant way of doing it! When the meal was over, the General Manager said — "I realise that you have only been in

Japan for five days, but in that short time, have you been able to see any of our Japanese culture and if so, what were your impressions?". I told him that my lasting impression of Japanese culture was soy sauce. There was much grave nodding of heads and nasal noises to greet this profound announcement. I spoke from the heart. Without the liberal use of this splendid brown liquid, I could never have attempted the meal.

In May 1985, we learned of further interest in our B35 from Yugo Oceanska and arranged a meeting in London. Things looked promising and soon afterwards these owners inspected the vessel in Sunderland. The contract was signed on 24th May for a price considerably in excess of the market price but considerably less than the original contract price. It had taken 17 months to sell.

The Corporate Plan issued to the Government in May referred to the timetable for the privatisation of the Naval Yards. The aim was to complete all sales by October 1986. By then, the Corporation would be a shadow of its former self, employing some 6,000/7,000 people. It would not by then have the benefit of warship-builders' profits to cushion the rest of the Corporation's losses. I felt sure that once this stage had been reached, the end was near for most of merchant shipbuilding in the U.K. 6,000/7,000 unemployed people spread across the Clyde, Tyne & Wear and a few outposts would constitute no threat to Government.

Compared with the previous somewhat hectic 18 months, the latter half of 1985 was fairly uneventful. Barge number 3 was launched on 11th September and delivered a few days later. On the last day of the month, our long-suffering B35 was handed over to the Yugoslavs at a very pleasant ceremony (*See illustration*). A month later barge number 4 was launched and in the following week was delivered to Knight's.

We had now constructed four identical barges, each one of them invaluable to us at the time. I remained in close touch with the original owners of barge number 1 — North Venture Shipping, as well as Smit and Knight's. About this time, Knights began talking about an altogether larger barge, one of 400 feet in length and with a beam of 120 feet, which would be required for a special project. We began to work up a price, but there was a problem. At 120 feet, it was too wide to fit into the complex and it was also too wide to fit our outside berths. I still wanted the work if we could get it. The

Christening the Yugoslav way! MV *Pomorac*, 30th September 1985.

solution was to widen the outside berth for part of its length. If we landed the contract we would then undertake this berth modification.

Meanwhile, the first Oldendorff ship was underway but earlier in the year there had been ominous signs that our Technical Department were making heavy weather of the development of the design. It was now clear that the owners had fundamentally changed the specification and our Technical Department could not advance sufficient argument for increasing the contract price. Moreover the issue of drawings to the yard were late.

It was approaching the festive season and as usual the Directors were hosting a Christmas Lunch for a number of business friends, including shipowners, shipbrokers, sub-contractors and surveyors. After the meal I occasionally tried to amuse our guests by reciting some doggerel concerning the current scenario in shipbuilding. The following is an extract:—

"When losses keep mounting the Cabinet say,
We're not permitting the public to pay,
Regardless of party, the cure is the same,
Reduction in numbers, the bosses to blame,
The shipbuilding body has over the years,
Lost an arm and a leg and a couple of ears,
It's a wonder to those of us left in the race,
That it functions at all with a good heart in place.
It really is difficult to see how one saves,
Industries managed by more chiefs than braves,
The Mandarins sit there, they huff and they puff,
Devoid of experience in industrial stuff,
In most heavy industries, I'm told it's the same,
Industrial suicide's the name of the game".

I returned to work after the New Year holiday to be told a few days later in Knightsbridge that with effect from 1st April 1986, A & P was to be merged with Sunderland Shipbuilders. The new company was to be called, North East Shipbuilders Limited and I was to be its Managing Director.

CHAPTER 19

NORTH EAST SHIPBUILDERS LIMITED

SUNDERLAND Shipbuilders Limited Consisted of three ship-yards — Pallion, North Sands and Deptford. Pallion, like A & P, was a superb shipbuilding factory, complete with a totally enclosed level building dock, large enough to construct two 12,000 ton deadweight cargo vessels side by side. The outfit shops were grouped around the dock with direct access to the ships under construction. The steel preparation areas and fabrication shed were almost on a par with A & P. This facility had been constructed on the site of the old Doxford yard, exactly opposite A & P.

The North Sands yard was the name given to the old J. L. Thompson's yard and was located some distance down river on the North bank, below Wearmouth Bridge. Its outfit shops were no longer in use since Sunderland Shipbuilders had centralised their joinery and piping facilities, It possessed a fairly large conventional slipway suitably craned, together with steel preparation shops and a fabrication shed. These steel facilities were in use, as was the long outfit jetty lying adjacent to the shipyard.

Deptford yard was located half a mile down river from the Pallion yard. It was by this time all but redundant.

Sunderland Shipbuilders had only three contracts but each of them was large and complex. Pallion had two — diving support vessels for Stena Line of Sweden, while North Sands had an enormous cranebarge for I.T.M. of Middlesbrough. The first Stena vessel was fitting out afloat while the second vessel was at an

164

advanced stage of construction in the Pallion dock. The cranebarge
was approaching launch.

No sooner had the announcement of my appointment been made
than the Corporation named the N.E.S.L. Board Members. As
before, there was no prior consultation. Only two of my colleagues
on the Board of A & P were nominated to the Board of N.E.S.L. —
that of the Finance and Technical Directors. Two members of the
new Board had been Sunderland Shipbuilders' Directors, one being
its Managing Director. They became Production and Planning
Director respectively. The remaining two Directors came from
H.Q. and were appointed Commercial and Industrial Relations
Director respectively.

There was no disputing that the main office of N.E.S.L. had to be
located in Pallion's offices since A & P's offices were altogether too
small. Although N.E.S.L. was not planned to come into being until
1st April, I immediately found myself submerged in discussions
concerning organisation charts for each Board Member. A Review
Group was set up for the purpose of deciding which facilities would
be retained. Duplication of facilities had to be avoided. Then there
was the question of staff salaries, which clearly required some
adjustment in order to bring these into line. A grading structure was
proposed.

Meanwhile on 26th February 1986, we signed a contract for the
large barge with Knight's of Rochester. Work was immediately put
in hand to widen A & P's outside berth. On 26th March the first
Oldendorff ship was launched without ceremony.

While the Review Group was meeting frequently at either Pallion
or Benton House, all the usual Corporation meetings continued to
take place. It was the time of the year for the Corporate Plan to
begin to take shape. Meetings on this, together with company
budgets were frequently held.

Before I knew it, it was 1st April 1986 and N.E.S.L. was in being.
All the senior staff were in place and most of the junior staff. We
had decided on the facilities to be retained. Two things worried me.
First, I detected that there might be some difficulties in the months
ahead in trying to mould the Board Members into a team. Second,
the little I had heard of the Stena and I.T.M. contracts concerned
me greatly.

On 2nd April, one of the Corporation's marketing people in

London rang to say that they had heard that a Danish businessman could be interested in placing orders for no less than 24 small ferries. He added that he had never heard of this man whose name was Zacchi and seriously doubted his intentions. He left me two telephone numbers to ring in Denmark if I wanted to follow up this so-called enquiry. I rang up straight away and a voice in perfect English said — "Just hang on a minute please, while I pull into a layby!". In the conversation that followed I learned that Peter Zacchi was deadly serious about ordering these ferries and that a number of different European yards had been asked to quote. It was clear that we were very late if we wished to enter the race. I asked whether I could come and see him. "Certainly, when would you like to see me?". I said — "What's wrong with tomorrow?" — and so it was arranged.

Two of us flew out to Copenhagen the next morning, arriving early in the afternoon. We were met at the airport by Peter Zacchi and driven to a hotel in the centre of Copenhagen. There we talked until midnight, stopping only for the occasional Danish open sandwich and a drink. Peter Zacchi was an extremely engaging chap and had conceived a novel ferry concept. With great enthusiasm he outlined its basic features to us. It was certainly novel but of course it needed to be developed into a finite design. He told us that he was working in conjunction with another businessman in Copenhagen, who would in fact be the owner of the vessels. Peter Zacchi was acting as his accredited agent and would be responsible amongst other things for developing the full specification and ultimately participate in the contract negotiations. He would in addition, personally superintend the construction of the ferries. His partner had positively identified the need for at least eight ferries which he would operate on an inter-island service within Danish waters. The remaining ferries he proposed to either charter out or sell to other interested parties. They were in no doubt that there would be World-wide interest in the novel design.

We hit it off with Peter Zacchi right from the start. We met again for breakfast the next day and talked until leaving for the airport. By this time we had decided to "enter the race" and invited him across to Sunderland to see our first-class facilities for himself. We explained the Corporations's set-up and how we operated within it. Most importantly, we explained the credit facilities available and the Intervention Fund subsidy. He was very interested and promised to visit us within a fortnight.

On our return, work immediately got underway in the Design Office and soon afterwards in the Drawing Office. It was a difficult period because we had no plans of any kind available to us. Continual telephone conversations between Denmark and Sunderland gradually developed the concept into a workable design. The ferries were named *Superflex Mark III* and *Superflex Mark IV*. The 12 Mark III ferries were designed to carry 24 40-ton trailers, 40 cars and 253 day passengers. The 12 Mark IV ferries were designed to carry 16 40-ton trailers 90 cars and 293 day passengers.

Peter Zacchi arrived in London on 15th April and joined our other guests on the N.E.S.L. table at the Royal Institution of Naval Architects Annual Dinner. He was conspicuous in a white tuxedo! Afterwards we all returned to Sunderland where Peter Zacchi remained until the following weekend. He spent most of this period buried in our Design Office, ironing out difficulties and generally helping to progress the technical development. The following week he returned to Sunderland for another session.

By the middle of May, plans were well underway in the Drawing Office and the estimators were busy preparing an estimate of price. We visited Copenhagen on 15th May and met the owner in his office, in the centre of the city. By this point it was clear that Peter Zacchi would try to steer the order our way, given of course that our price was reasonably competitive. He certainly had not spent any time in any of our competitors' yards.

By the beginning of June, we had calculated a rough price and at this point brought the Corporation's Commercial Director into the picture. He was the man responsible for liaising with the D.T.I. on the question of subsidy.

If we won this business, our intention was to construct all 12 Mark III vessels at Pallion and all 12 Mark IV vessels at A & P. The crucial question was, what productivity rate did we assume for the first of each class and what improvements could be achieved over the run of 12 ships? There was a great deal of heart-searching by the Board over this matter. Naturally we were closely questioned on this and all other costs making up the price by the Corporation's Commercial Director. Various amendments were made.

The owner wished to see a specimen Corporation contract in

order that he could study its terms. This was sent to him and on
12th June we flew back to Copenhagen to discuss this document.
The owner then explained how he intended to finance the contract.
I thought at the time that it was a pretty nifty piece of footwork!

Towards the end of that month the owner, accompanied by Peter
Zacchi, arrived in Sunderland. The price of each ferry was
discussed and it seemed that we were were close to agreement. But
the unusual payment terms requested by the owner required further
study by the Corporation's Commercial Director. The owner at this
point proposed fundamental amendments to the contract which we
could not accept and the meeting terminated in considerable
acrimony. I learned the next day from Peter Zacchi that he had
been distressed at the manner in which the meeting had ended and
assured me that he would do everything he could to persuade his
colleague to modify some of his demands. But he stressed that we,
for our part, must do likewise.

I was booked to fly to Corfu on holiday on 30th June. Before
leaving I gave instructions that no further price reductions could be
considered and suggested the limits of any concessions to the
contract terms. The financing and payment terms I left in the hands
of the Corporation's Commercial Director.

I returned from holiday to Manchester airport at 3.00 a.m. on
Monday, 14th July and was met by our driver. He handed me a
sheaf of documents all in connection with the ferries. Apparently I
was supposed to read these complex papers immediately before
catching a flight to London from Newcastle in a few hours time and
on which I had already been booked. Peter Zacchi was to arrive in
Knightsbridge that morning and it was imperative that this meeting
take place.

I didn't attempt to read the papers in the back of a car at
4.00 a.m. heading North up the A1! Instead, I fell asleep. Once
home, I changed my flight to later that morning and arranged to
join the meeting in Knightsbridge about lunchtime. En-route to
London, I tried hard to comprehend the contents of the documents.
They were all Side Letters to the contract and gave effect to various
payment terms and related matters. Our team, particularly the
Corporation's Commercial Director had been working overtime!

The next three days were spent in Knightsbridge refining the
documentation and on Friday, 18th July, Peter Zacchi and I signed

the contract for 24 ferries worth some £93,000,000 (*See illustration*). The last ferry was scheduled for delivery in December 1989 and so we now had three years work for 1,650 men and one of the best order books in the world.

I have spent some time describing the negotiations leading up to signing this large contract, because this business occupied a fair bit of my time over the period from 2nd April until 18th July. In any case, it was remarkably short space of time in which to complete negotiations for a contract. This business apart, I was busy on other matters. Perhaps the most important of these were the monthly managing Director's Reports to the Corporation. Prior to these reports being drafted, it was necessary to convene a Contract Appraisal Meeting, at which each contract was discussed in detail and an assessment made of likely final costs. These meetings frequently lasted for most of one day. The first of these took place on 7th April and then I began to understand something of the complexities of both the Stena and Cranebarge contracts.

The Oldendorff contracts were falling behind and costs were rising alarmingly.

The first Stena vessel was nearing completion and a "Press Open Day" was held on board the ship on 14th April. Eleven days later, the ship was named by the Prime Minister, Margaret Thatcher.

Meanwhile there were Corporation Management Committee Meetings to attend each month. Sales meetings were convened also on a monthly basis. As if we didn't have enough to occupy our time, a further Team Building Seminar was organised outside Carlisle in early May.

By this time it appeared that the Stena contracts and the Cranebarge were running reasonably to programme and that the problem was with Oldendorff. Since the two Stena contracts in particular had reached a reasonably advanced condition, I saw no reason for taking over any outstanding contractual or technical discussions with these owners. These discussions had been conducted up to now by the ex-Managing Director of Sunderland Shipbuilders (and now the Production Director), assisted by the Planning Director. For the same reason, I did not interfere in similar discussions with the Cranebarge owners. In any case, I do not believe that I could have done justice to such work after only eight weeks at N.E.S.L. and with all the other matters demanding my attention.

Signing the Danish ferry contract at Knightsbridge, 18th July 1986.

Among many things obsessing the Corporation at this time was the notion of "Project Management". The Planning Director claimed to have been operating in such a way prior to the merger, in relation to both Stena ships and the Cranebarge. The Corporation was adamant that the Danish ferry contracts should be organised on a project management basis. Accordingly ,the Planning Director became Project Manager for the Danish ships as well. What a time to introduce such changes!

Suddenly, a number of shocks occurred in quick succession. The first Stena ship returned from sea trials, having failed to satisfactorily operate a number of its complex systems. About the same time I.T.M., the owners of the Cranebarge, went into Receivership. So far as Stena was concerned, a meeting was convened in their Gothenberg offices, where they made it clear that, until the systems were fully operational, there could be no question of their accepting the vessel for which they claimed that they now had lined up some profitable business. The very onerous payment terms forming part of the contract ensured that a substantial proportion of the price was not payable to N.E.S.L. until delivery had been achieved. So far as the Cranebarge was concerned, we now had a £50,000,000 contract almost at launch stage, but with no owner.

It was at this point that I became quite disillusioned about the whole business. By now, the Corporation had been reduced to Govan Shipbuilders, Appledore and N.E.S.L. Smiths Dock was to be closed shortly. This meant that the Corporation Staff, who had not been reduced in proportion, concentrated their energies on us. There was no respite. From then on it was uphill all the way.

Phillip Hares, the Corporation Board Member for Finance, had succeeded Graham Day (later Sir Graham) as Chairman. Henning Oldendorff invited Mrs. Hares to be sponsor of his second ship, which was programmed to be launched on the same day as the first ship was to be commissioned and named. The double event was to be organised for no less than 300 guests and was timed for 3rd November.

Meanwhile, towards the end of August, we were pressurised further by the Corporation in the shape of a Performance Review Meeting. In view of the way that our contracts were falling apart, the board of N.E.S.L. had two rehearsals! The Managing Director's Monthly Reports were now indicating serious losses due to severe technical and contractual problems with Stena, the assumed "fire sale" of the Cranebarge and the escalating costs of Oldendorff. I privately thought that the Corporation could not reasonably attribute any blame to me for the first two, but most certainly could and would for the latter. I felt pretty sure that this situation would not be allowed to continue for much longer. Incidentally, there was no effort on the part of the Corporation's Board to assist us. It was still very much an arm's length relationship with communication based largely on written reports.

By the end of October, we had decided to take legal advice on the matter of the Stena contracts. Meanwhile, the Corporation's Commercial Director had taken over responsibility for trying to find new owners for the Cranebarge.

The high points of November were the Oldendorff "double event" which proved highly successful, the signing of a contract for a 25th Danish ferry and the spectacular launch without ceremony of the Cranebarge. The remainder of 1986 passed in a kaleidoscope of legal meetings about Stena, Oldendorff delayed delivery and increased costs together with the Corporation's concern about the Danish ferry programme. By Christmas I was sick of it!

It was all over by 10th February 1987. The Corporation were clearly under intense pressure from Government to reduce losses, especially at N.E.S.L. I was asked to step down, which I did without question. No reason was given. The grand gesture had now been made for Government's benefit.

I had enjoyed a long innings and had survived longer than most, if not all of my ex-colleagues in the industry. I had in the course of 40 years "won a few and lost a few". The majority of it had been hugely enjoyable and through most of it I had done shipbuilding — my way!

CHAPTER 20

A FEW SHIPBUILDERS

THE senior chauffeur at Smiths Dock considered that I was working far harder than his late boss — Colonel Sir Eustace Smith. Apparently, Sir Eustace was uplifted each morning from his small estate some 20 miles distant from the shipyard and delivered to the offices by 10,00 a.m. The chauffeur, Potter by name, was extremely respectful as well as being the soul of discretion. He had been well trained for not only was he the Colonel's chauffeur but also his valet. His duties did not stop there. During the shooting season for example, he was required to organise and serve the picnic lunches, reload the guns and generally ensure the well-being of his employer at all times.

Each year the Colonel would take Lady Smith in the Bentley to Norway, driven of course, by Potter. Going by sea from Newcastle to Bergen, they would then call on shipowners all the way round the coast — Stavanger, Kristiansand, Grimstad, Larvik, Tonsberg to Oslo. They would host dinner parties, which were reciprocated and enjoy a spot of fishing with their shipowning friends. Such was the lifestyle of one shipbuilding proprietor.

Not only did the Colonel own and run an extremely profitable shipbuilding and shiprepairing business, he was also a very good and considerate employer. Many of the staff and employees had spent a lifetime with the company, which bore witness to this fact.

Another notable shipbuilding proprietor of yesteryear was Mr. Henry Lithgow, brother of Sir James. While Sir James was concerned with his various business interests beyond the confines of

173

Port Glasgow, he remained a very active Chairman of the company that bore his name. Travelling extensively in the U.K., he left the day-to-day running of the two shipyards to his brother.

Mr. Henry Lithgow was a shy retiring man of simple tastes who loved to build ships. Like his elder brother, he also loved shooting and deer stalking on the family estate at Ormsary, near Lochgilphead in Argyllshire. In the shooting season, promptly at 5.00 p.m. on a Friday, he would emerge from the offices and settle himself in his open touring car and would then be driven to the estate arriving some hours later.

Willie Andrews, the Head Foreman Joiner at Lithgows for many years, took up the story. Mr. Henry sent for him one Friday afternoon and asked him to come and inspect a second-hand caravan that he had just purchased. The interior was pretty scruffy and he was instructed to strip it out and install — "a simple bed, a single basic wardrobe, an upright chair, a small strip of carpet and a set of blinds". He enquired whether Andrews could undertake the job in one week, since he intended using the caravan to transport him to Ormsary.

This settled, he left Andrews to it. It wasn't too often that Andrews was asked to undertake work for Mr. Henry and he went at it with gusto. He panelled the walls, manufactured and installed a high-class bed with headboard, an elaborate wardrobe complete with drawers, tie-rack and mirror, bought an easy chair and carpeted the interior wall-to-wall — and as a final touch, provided curtains. By the following Friday afternoon, the interior had been polished and awaited Mr. Henry's inspection. He took one look at it and stepped outside. He didn't raise his voice, but merely said — "Andrews, kindly strip all this out at once and provide me please with what I asked for in the first place".

Suitably chastened, Andrews produced the sparse interior requested and on the Friday following Mr. Henry politely accepted his new charge. From that point on, during the shooting season, Mr. Henry emerged from the offices at 5.00 p.m. on a Friday but stepped not into the car, but into the caravan. The driver was under instructions to drive at no more than 30 miles per hour thus allowing Mr. Lithgow to go to sleep. On arrival at Ormsary in the early hours, the caravan would be towed to the edge of the grouse moor and the car unhitched and driven back to the house. Mr.

Lithgow meanwhile slept on undisturbed, only to be woken by the driver who brought him a hot breakfast. Thus refreshed, he was ready to receive his shooting guests.

The Lithgow brothers also enjoyed the benefit of a grouse moor near their homes outside Port Glasgow. There, for the convenience of shooting guests, they had a narrow-gauge railway constructed. The passengers sat astride the coaches while being conveyed across the moor. Someone who knew the Lithgows well compared the success of their shipbuilding business with the manner in which the railway was run — "Sir James is in the driving seat with the throttle wide open, while Mr. Henry is in the guard's van with the brakes fully on. Thus the train and the company make steady progress!"

Like Sir Eustace Smith, the Lithgow brothers were highly respected and were very good employers. They built many houses in Port Glasgow for the benefit of their employees and made countless substantial but anonymous donations to charities.

I have no doubt that the numerous other shipbuilding proprietors enjoyed a similar life-style. Life-style apart, they were professionals in their own way. Although their succession to the chairmanship had no doubt been assured and achieved without the need for laboriously climbing each rung of the promotion ladder, they were nonetheless expert at marketing and selling. In order to achieve success in these fields, they had to be alive to the vagaries of the shipping market as well as having a wide circle of shipowning contacts.

The shipbuilding businesses that were public companies were mostly run by professional shipbuilders, many of whom had started from humble beginnings and moved from yard to yard gaining experience and promotion with each move.

John Rannie for example, my boss at John Browns, started his career as an apprentice shipwright. The son of a policemen, he displayed such promise at night-school that his employer undertook to send him to university where he graduated with an M.Sc. degree.

After graduating, he spent two years as naval architect and estimator with Sociedad Española at Bilbao and returned to Clydebank as assistant shipyard manager in 1931. In 1936 he joined Lloyd's Register of Shipping and served in London, Barrow, Denmark, New York, Mobile and San Francisco. In 1942, he was appointed shipyard manager of the Victoria Machinery Depot Ltd., in British Columbia and a few months later became manager of United Shipyards, Montreal. In 1944 he was asked to return to Clydebank. Not long afterwards he succeeded Sir Donald Skiffington as Shipyard Director, where he directed shipyard production and labour relations for close on 20 years. He was then appointed Managing Director and in the process he became President of the Shipbuilding Employers Federation.

He was a character all right, with real "presence" when he entered a crowded room. Of striking appearance, he was large in stature with an appetite to match. He loved food but not of the exotic type — jugged hare and haggis were among his favourites. He hadn't any hobbies except gardening where he specialised in growing gourds. One of his endearing features was his total inability to tell a joke correctly — it was all the more hilarious for that!

Bill Dawson, the Secretary of the Clyde Shipbuilders Association for many years, was a lawyer by training. But by "absorption" he became a shipbuilder. He was highly respected for his sharp mind and uncanny ability to instantly spot a weakness in any union claim. He was not just a destroyer of claims however. He could construct solutions to seemingly intractable labour disputes with consummate ease. He was a friend of shipbuilders not only on the Clyde but elsewhere in the U.K. He was a good storyteller and loved parties. He was a low handicap golfer and was in his element at the Annual Golf Tournament of the Shipbuilding Employers Federation.

One year the event was being held at Gleneagles. The format for these outings followed an established pattern. Shipbuilders and their wives would assemble in time for afternoon tea, following which there was a dinner — one for the gentleman and one next door for the ladies. After dinner, having rejoined the ladies, bets would be placed on the golf participants, the odds having been established by two shipbuilders acting as bookmakers. It was late in the night before the last light went out.

This particular year, Bill Dawson together with a number of other shipbuilders had spent many hours in the bar. My father witnessed what happened next, from his armchair outside the hotel billiard room. In the distance he heard much shouting and laughing and thundering footsteps. Into view along the wide corridor came

Dawson, hotly pursued by his cronies. Just as he was about to be caught, Dawson deftly side-stepped into the billiard room where two elderly gentlemen were enjoying a quiet and serious game of snooker. Without stopping, Dawson scooped up the cueball and continued on his way, leaving the gaping and infuriated brigadiers to the mercies of the horde following. It was not reported how the ensuing complaint was dealt with.

Be that as it may, Dawson and company continued their high jinks for several more hours before finally retiring. Since Dawson was timed to be on the 1st Tee at 9.00 a.m., he rang down to reception and asked to be called at 7.30 a.m. By 8.45 a.m. he had still not appeared for breakfast and so John Rannie volunteered to hurry him up. He found Dawson sound asleep still in his evening clothes. Another feature of Dawson's make-up was his astounding recuperative powers. As soon as he was awake, he insisted on having words with the hotel receptionist for her apparent negligence in not carrying out his instructions. He asked the receptionist to confirm that he had requested a call at 7.30 a.m. She confirmed this, but added that she really hadn't felt he was serious since his telephone request had been made at 6.45 a.m.!

He was on the 1st Tee at 9.15 a.m. where his golf bag was stuffed with 18 small bottles of lemonade — one for each hole — for the purpose of relieving some of the dehydration!

Andrew Paxton was a good friend of mine and was Managing Director of The Greenock Dockyard Co. Ltd. Unusual for a shipyard, it was owned by a large U.K. shipping company — British & Commonwealth, who operated the Union Castle Mail and passenger service to South Africa. They also operated the Clan Line with a large fleet of cargo liners. All the later Clan Line vessels were built at this yard and elegant ships they were.

Andrew served his apprenticeship with William Denny & Bros. Ltd., of Dumbarton and worked his way "up the greasy pole". He was a big man with a colourful face and language to match. Energetic and diligent, he was a very good shipbuilder indeed. He forced the pace and had many adventures with his shop stewards.

I met him one morning at the James Watt Dock in Greenock. I could see that he was dying to tell me something and was grinning from ear to ear. He said — "The vice-convener of shop stewards came up to me earlier this morning and announced that the convener would not be able to attend the meeting called for later today because he had been taken ill. Do you know what I said?" — "Nothing trivial I hope!".

Andrew and I were two of the four Clyde members of the Conference and Works Board of the Shipbuilding Employers Federation. We normally flew down from Glasgow to London together on the previous evening. Occasionally, we visited Raymond's Review Bar, which in those days was considered quite risqué. To gain entrance, one had to fill in a membership application and wait for some days before being issued with a membership card. We always managed to see the show without waiting for the card. On one occasion, another colleague signed his application in the name of the General Secretary of the Boilermakers Union. That card, if delivered to its destination, may or may not have been well received! I signed my application in the name of a friend and neighbour. Neither of us imagined that the cards would be delivered. Later I was confronted by the irate wife of my friend and neighbour. I think she thought that I was trying to corrupt her husband.

One morning on my way to work at Lithgows, I was astounded to see the *Clan MacIver*, berthed under the heavy crane in the James Watt Dock, heeled over at a really dangerous angle. The ship was nearing completion and was of course, one of Andrew's babies. I drove the car to the other side of the Dock and literally looked down the funnel!

The accident had occurred sometime during the night, but by 8.00 a.m., Clydeside humour had already registered its mark. At the time, one of the commonest cigarette advertisements read — "Let Capstan take the strain". Some foolhardy humourist had managed somehow to paint across the stern of the ship in huge white letters — "Let Paxton take the strain!".

Hugh Currie was another good friend. Born and bred in Port Glasgow, he joined Lithgows as a messenger boy at the age of fifteen. He later served his apprenticeship as a ship draughtsman and was eventually transferred to the estimating and design office, where in due course he became chief designer. This was when I first came across him. He went on to become Technical Manager and when Scotts merged with Lithgows to form Scott-Lithgow Ltd., he was promoted to Director and General Manager of the Lithgow portion of the Group.

He was unpretentious although proud of his humble background. A highly developed sense of humour saved him on numerous occasions from almost certain dismissal on account of some outrageous comment made against those in authority. His warmth and humour were quite infectious and charmed "Dukes and Dustmen alike". He made many friends, not only in the local community, but also among the shipowning fraternity.

While I was doing a spell in the Design and Estimating Office at Lithgows, Hugh and I were despatched to Wageningin in Holland, for the purpose of witnessing the model tests of a bulk carrier. Accompanied by two owners' representatives we were shown into an elegant wood-panelled waiting room. Shortly afterwards, a party of Dutch officials entered the room, led by Dr. Van Manen, the distinguished Naval Architect. The Doctor smiled at Hugh, gave a slight bow, clicked his heels, proffered his hand and said — "Van Manen". Hugh did likewise and to everyone's amazement also said — "Van Manen". He apparently thought that "Van Manen" was Dutch for "Good Morning!". Such are the advantages of a primary Port Glasgow education!

One morning, Leonard Boden, a Director of Rowan & Boden, the Glasgow ship furnishing concern, looked into the Design and Estimating Office. Before discussing business, the conversation centred upon the news of the latest football pool winner. Turning to Hugh, Leonard Boden said — "What would you do Hugh, if you won £75,000 in the pools?". Quick as a flash, Hugh replied — "I'd put £25,000 to it and buy one of your three piece suites!".

Hugh and I managed to persuade Alec White, at that time Managing Director of Lithgows, to sanction a company-sponsored annual golf tournament. Turnberry was chosen as the venue and the hotel bookings made. Alec White selected the menu for the opening dinner and this selection included Vichyssoise soup. We were all duly seated at the table when Alec White called for grace to be said. Everyone stood up and Alec White said "Thank God". Everyone continued standing up, eyes closed. Seconds passed and on opening our eyes we saw Alec half way through his soup! All of us began to devour the soup all that is except Hugh. He complained to Alec White — "I can't eat this — it's stone cold!". West Chapelton School, Port Glasgow, certainly had a lot to answer for!

Provost Walter Lucas of Port Glasgow had been a confidante of

Sir James and Mr. Henry Lithgow in times past and continued to maintain close contact with Alec White and other Lithgow Directors. In 1812, Henry Bell had built his famous *Comet* in Port Glasgow and the Provost thought it would be no bad thing for the town if a replica could be constructed by Lithgows to celebrate the 150th Anniversary of this great achievement. It was agreed that Lithgows would build the hull and John G. Kincaid, the Greenock Marine Engineers would build the machinery. Working from the little information that was available, the ship was duly constructed. In the case of Kincaid's, the *Comet*'s engine was located inside a glass case in the Science Museum in London, but the Curator flatly refused to permit Kincaid's Chief Draughtsman access to its interior! Somehow the engine was manufactured.

Amid much publicity, the date was set for the voyage of the new *Comet* across the Firth of Clyde from Princes Pier at Greenock to Helensburgh Pier. It was planned to leave around 1.00 p.m. and return to Greenock in the early evening. The sun shone in a cloudless sky as an armada of yachts assembled to greet this tiny boat with its tall smokestack.

Provost Lucas led a select group of dignitaries aboard. They included the young Sir William Lithgow, the Managing Director of John G. Kincaid and others. They were all attired in period costumes — tall hats, frock coats and buckled shoes. I was able to witness the events of the day at close quarters, because Hugh Currie, my brother Cameron and I were placed aboard the Press Launch, which was scheduled to "shadow" this epic voyage. The Press Launch like the *Comet* was equipped with a small cabin but alas lacked a commodity the *Comet* possessed in abundance — whisky!

The star of the show made an uneventful, if slow and smoky passage to Helensburgh, its passengers thoroughly enjoying the sunshine, the attention and the contents of the hamper placed at their disposal. On arrival at Helensburgh Pier, we were met by the town's Provost, resplendent in a lavender frock coat. He was taking snuff! A waiting stage-coach conveyed the dignitaries to a local hotel, while we followed in more modern transport.

Everyone joined in the spirit of the occasion. After cocktails and a good meal, a number of amusing speeches were made. After several hours of merriment, it was back to Helensburgh Pier for the return voyage. Some little time after setting out, the engine of the *Comet* decided it needed a rest! At the same time, the sky darkened and it began to rain — lightly at first. As the Kincaid engineers struggled to revive the engine, it grew dark and the rain began to fall in earnest. Eventually, the *Comet* got underway and we looked across to see its now unenthusiastic passengers sitting huddled in the tiny cabin against the elements, top hats crumpled and dripping and worst of all — an empty hamper! The homecoming was not quite in the style of the send-off. But it certainly had been a memorable day and Provost Lucas, wet and weary as he must have been, I'm sure was a happy man. The *Comet* replica incidentally, still stands proudly near the main road through Port Glasgow.

"Basher" Wadkin was C.S.C.B.S. Translated that meant — Commodore Superintendent Contract Built Ships. Further translation revealed that he was the sole Naval Officer that accepted or otherwise, on behalf of the Ministry of Defence (Navy), surface naval vessels built in the U.K.

"Basher" was a man "born out of his time". He was straight out of Sir Francis Drake, Grenville and other Englishmen that "ruled the waves". He was a man of medium height but of immense breadth and in his fifties. He was literally bursting out of his Naval uniform emblazoned with the single broad stripe of a Commodore. In earlier years, he had played rugby for the Mediterranean Fleet. He was a truly tremendous personality and was welcomed and respected by all Naval builders.

My first experience of his activities occurred soon after my arrival at John Brown's yard with the delivery of H.M.S.. *Hampshire*, a guided-missile destroyer. "Basher" arrived at Clydebank at 8.00 a.m. carrying an overnight case. He quickly changed into a boilersuit and accompanied by ship's officers and shipyard personnel, made his way to the ship. Then began a whirlwind tour of every compartment. Access between compartments on naval ships can only be gained through vertical ladders. No access was available to adjacent compartments on the same level. After inspecting twelve compartments which involved four sets of vertical ladders, "Basher" was perspiring profusely. He opened lockers, looked under bunks, shone his torch over the ceilings obscured by electric cables, barked the occasional question and pressed on. At 10.30 he called for a break. Coffee was served and in his case, heavily laced with rum. The short break over, he excused himself and a few moments later reappeared in a fresh shirt and boilersuit, ready to resume his inspection. It was all over by 1.00 p.m. — five hours of sustained mental and physical application. Over lunch, he was an entertaining guest with a repertoire of anecdotes, naval and otherwise.

I felt less overwhelmed when, two years later, he returned to Clydebank to inspect H.M.S. *Aurora*, a Leander class frigate. One of the curious requirements of the Navy in those days, was the "finish" of the machinery space bilges. They had to be painted in gloss white paint. When the machinery was in use, the bilges of course, were swimming in oily water. So, after final machinery trials, all this sludge had to be cleaned up and the bilges carefully painted, avoiding coating the brass hand valves which had to be burnished bright.

"Basher" carried out his usual and "individual" inspection. When he reached the boiler-room bilges, he expressed himself highly satisfied with the quality of the paintwork. In fact, we received a special commendation for the standard achieved. When, a few weeks later, the ship ran Acceptance Trials, "Basher" suggested that the ship be officially handed over off Ailsa Craig on the Firth of Clyde at full speed rather than alongside the jetty on completion of trials. I found myself near the stern of the ship in the company of "Basher" with a glass of champagne in my hand. A great vertical wall of water rose up from the stern as the ship sped up the Firth of Clyde at 30 knots, while the vibration over the twin screws was responsible for partly emptying my glass. Later that evening at dinner, he was his usual entertaining self.

He referred to a brother officer who had served with him in the Mediterranean Fleet before the War. This officer, who was also a rugby player of note was of Polynesian extraction I think from Fiji. Apparently he was proud of the fact that his grandparents had been cannibals! Flying out with Imperial Airways to rejoin his ship, he was approached by a steward, who asked — "If you're hungry sir, I can show you the menu". The reply was — "Yes I am, but I'd prefer to see the Passenger List!".

CHAPTER 21

TWO "TRUE BLUE" SHIPOWNERS

Blue Funnel Line

SADLY, over the period of the last 15 years or so, some of this country's biggest shipowners have vanished from the scene. Some others have shrunk to a shadow of their former size. Many were household names. The reasons for their disappearance were a combination of U.K. tax disincentives, subsidized and expanding competition and cargo preference arrangements practised by a number of countries. One of the best-known and respected shipowning companies in the first category was Alfred Holt & Co. Ltd., of Liverpool.

This famous company commenced operations in 1865 with a new vessel — the *Agamemnon*, built by Scotts of Greenock. She set out on her maiden voyage to China on 19th April, 1866. The company owning the vessel was named the Ocean Steamship Company. To this company were added in later years the China Mutual Steam Navigation Co. Ltd., Nederlandsche Stoomvaart Maatschappij "Oceaan" N.V., Amsterdam and the Glen Line Ltd., of London.

The ships normally loaded at Glasgow, Birkenhead and Swansea and served ports in Japan, through the China Coast, Hong Kong and Philippines, southwards through the territories of Borneo, Malaya and the islands of Indonesia to the Australian coast.

As mentioned earlier, my father had many dealings with the Blue Funnel Line or "Blue Flue" as they were known. The Caledon Yard in Dundee built a good number of their fleet, which after replacement of wartime losses, stood at some 80 ships. All but a handful were cargo liners of some 8,000 tons gross, built for the Far East trade. The company was well established at Far East ports and indeed owned or leased a number of wharves at some of them. As a consequence, if a particular port was full, with ships anchored in the bay awaiting a berth, such hold-ups did not apply to Blue Funnel ships.

The company's Australian liner service was maintained by larger turbine-driven vessels of the *Helenus* and *Ixion* classes, each of which carried a number of passengers. A single vessel — the *Telemachus*, maintained a service between North America and the Far East, while two vessels, built pre-war by the Caledon yard — the *Gorgon* and *Charon*, carried out a most unusual service between Fremantle in Western Australia and Singapore. These vessels, in addition to carrying passengers — mainly holidaying Australians, were equipped to carry live cattle and sheep to Singapore and latex and general cargo on the return voyage. At low tide in Fremantle harbour, the vessels were grounded and for this reason had specially strengthened keels.

The sea trials, final inspection and delivery procedures adopted by these owners in respect of Caledon-built ships never varied. Sea trials were carried out in the Tay estuary, from early morning until early evening. The ship then returned and anchored opposite the shipyard, while those personnel not required for the voyage to Glasgow were ferried ashore.

Thereafter the ship steamed up the East Coast of Scotland, through the Pentland Firth and down the West Coast, finally docking at Barclay Curle's Elderslie Drydocks at Glasgow.

On completion of pre-delivery docking, the ship was towed a short distance up river to King George V Dock, her first loading berth. Prior to leaving, the ship was inspected from top to bottom by a team of owners' supervisors, led by the curiously named Shipwright General Manager. This position during the 50s was occupied by the fearsome W. H. Dickie, who, if things were not 100%, was scathing in his comments to the builders. This "crocodile" of inspectors examined every nook and cranny of the vessel in their thorough search for omissions.

Such work as was left was completed by the time the ship was loaded. Before sailing, the owner, Mr. Lawrence Holt, personally addressed the officers and crew. They were assembled on the

Shelter Dock, while Mr. Holt stood on the Poop. My father witnessed these proceedings on a number of occasions. Lawrence Holt opened his address by saying — "This vessel has been built to the high standards set by the company and has, throughout her construction been under the close supervision of the company's officials to ensure that these standards have been met. They are now fully satisfied with the vessel's condition. However, if any one of you can point to any fault in any part of the vessel, I undertake that such a fault will be corrected before sailing". No-one spoke. He continued — "So be it. You are now about to sail this fine new vessel to the other side of the World and I expect you to return her to this country at the end of the voyage in the condition in which you found her!".

In 1961, Caledon completed the last Blue Funnel ship that they would ever build. By this time, U.K. owners were turning their eyes to Japan, whose shipbuilders up to then had been categorized as builders of purely "simple" ships like tankers. Unfortunately for U.K. builders, the Japanese were beginning to emerge as high-quality builders of sophisticated ships as well.

In the meantime, Holt's placed an order for four cargo liners — two with Fairfield of Glasgow and two with Dutch shipbuilders. Shortly afterwards they finally committed themselves to Japan by placing orders for eight vessels of the *Glenalmond* class — five with Vickers Naval Yard on Tyneside, one with John Brown and two with Mitsubishi. The first of the new ships to be delivered was from Japan. I visited the ship in London on completion of her maiden voyage and was greatly impressed with the high quality of workmanship. Vickers made very heavy weather of their five vessels, notwithstanding their experience of building many ships for these owners. As far as our single vessel was concerned at Clydebank, we did not make too much heavy weather of the work but managed to make a big loss. Before any of the U.K.-built vessels had been completed, John Rannie joked to George Houlden, the boss of Vickers — "I know what loss you'll make on your ships — five times as much as our loss". It turned out to be a remarkably accurate prediction.

The two ships that maintained the Fremantle/Singapore link were, by the early 60s, getting long in the tooth and the owners decided to replace them by a single vessel, the order for which was

placed with John Brown. The ship named *Centaur* was only 435
feet in length, but hugely complicated. It was powered by twin
B & W engines and equipped with fin stabilizers. Accommodation
was provided for 200 passengers with public room facilities and an
outdoor swimming pool and lido. Two of the holds were
refrigerated and a deep tank for the carriage of latex was provided.
The lower and upper 'tweendecks were fitted out for the transport
of livestock. They consisted of a number of aluminium cattle pens,
complete with strip lighting and strict temperature control. Each
pen was fitted with an aluminium platform stowed under the
deckhead when cattle were being carried, or lowered to half height
to accommodate sheep on each level.

It proved a difficult ship to fit out and that took no account of
the fearsome Blue Funnel supervision! Nearing completion , I
learned that a well-known sculptor had been commissioned by the
owners to produce his vision of *Centaur*. This bronze object was to
be fixed to the bulkhead forming the back of the aft staircase in the
passenger accommodation. It was decided to hang "the thing"
during the lunch hour, under the supervision of the sculptor. After
lunch, I went onboard to have a look and nearly died laughing.
Centaur is of course half-man and half-horse. One wag had already
stuck a fag in its mouth and attached some loo paper to its rear end.
It improved it!

The *Glenalmond* class were the last cargo liners built for Alfred
Holt. Containerisation was coming on stream and high class cargo
liners became redundant. Holt's combined with P & O and British
and Commonwealth to form Overseas Containers Ltd., (O.C.L.)
and in 1969 ordered a series of large fast and expensive container
ships in West Germany. Meanwhile the cargo liner fleet was being
sold off. A further four even larger containerships were ordered in
1972 again from West Germany and further units have been added
since. The O.C.L. fleet of some twenty vessels is indeed impressive
in terms of capacity and technology.

In 1978, Holt's (or Ocean Transport & Trading P.L.C. to give
them their new name), ordered six — 21,000 ton deadweight
multi-purpose cargo vessels for the their Elder Dempster Line's
service to West Africa. Four were placed with Mitsubishi and two
with Scott-Lithgow on the Clyde.

These were to be the last ships ordered by the company. In the early 80s, the company took the decision to sell off its fleet and concentrate on other related activities. So ended the shipowning activities of one of the most famous U.K. companies.

Blue Star Line

Among prominent British shipowners, Blue Star Line Ltd., had an altogether shorter history, but interesting nonetheless. Operations commenced in 1911 with three refrigerated cargo vessels voyaging in the main to China and South America.

In 1926, the company established a regular mail and passenger service to South America with five new twin-screw turbine-driven liners of some 14,500 tons gross. One of these, the *Arandora Star* was later converted into a cruise liner and with her white hull, red ribband and colourful funnel was christened "chocolate box" by the travelling public, with whom she quickly became very popular.

By the outbreak of World War II, the fleet had grown to 38 ships. Of these only nine remained at the end of hostilities. The story of M.V. *Melbourne Star*'s epic survival from repeated German air attacks on the convoy bound with precious food and other materials to Malta has been told elsewhere.

Blue Star Line Ltd., is only one of many companies owned and directed by the Vestey family. The total enterprise straddles continents but the basic commodity is meat. In Australia, cattle and sheep are reared, slaughtered, stored in the company's cold stores to await transportation in the company's ships to the U.K. and other destinations. In the U.K. after discharge, the meat is again placed in company cold stores and much of it eventually finds its way to Dewhurst and Munro butcher shops, both Vestey companies. The company's enterprises included insurance and land owning, including a Highland hotel.

Up until recently the present generation of the Vestey family running this huge operation was Lord Sam Vestey and Mr. Edmund Vestey. I was privileged to get to know the latter well during my time at Smiths Dock starting in 1973. By this date, the fleet stood at around its pre-war level of some 35 vessels. The ordering of a new ship was not delegated to someone else in the organisation — Edmund Vestey was personally involved with the shipbuilder.

I found him to be at all times courteous, pleasant and helpful and when I had my troubles with the Haverton Hill labour force, very understanding and tolerant. Notwithstanding what I imagine was a huge workload, I was always able to see him by appointment, sometimes at less than 24 hours notice. He was invariably available at the precise time agreed.

The story goes that some years ago, Blue Star Line's Chief Engineer Superintendent asked to see Edmund Vestey's father Mr. R. A. Vestey, on a matter of great urgency. He explained, with considerable trepidation, that part of the refrigerated meat cargo discharged from a company vessel in London Docks was tainted with the smell of oranges. The oranges were apparently stowed in an adjacent compartment and presumably a fault, either in the refrigeration or insulation systems, had caused the problem. Apart from curing this problem, the more urgent matter was — What was to be the fate of the valuable tainted meat cargo now lying on the dockside? Mr. R. A. Vestey told his Superintendent that his decision on this question would be given within half an hour. Precisely 30 minutes later, the Superintendent was told to arrange for the part-cargo to be distributed to a member of the Dewhurst shops, whose managers had been instructed to sell the meat, but in so doing, offer free oranges with each meat sale. An ingenious solution to avert a possible loss!

I always felt that while some shipowners might "go to the wall" when cold economic winds were blowing, Blue Star Line would survive. Indeed there were two spectacular company collapses within the reefer trade — that of the Maritime Fruit Carriers of Israel and Salen of Sweden. The latter company was in the 70s the World's largest reefer operator. When the reefer market was good, the Vesteys did not immediately join the rush to place orders for new ships. New orders were placed, but only after much thought. No doubt the financial muscle wielded by the total enterprise helped to cushion Blue Star Line in periods of depression, but I remain convinced that the family tried to ensure that each company was entirely self supporting in financial terms.

Edmund Vestey was a very good listener and made much use of what he learned from those prepared to talk. Generally speaking, Bert Tune, the Chief Marine Superintendent, was generally speaking! I got to know him particularly well, together with his small, friendly and capable staff. They were to a man, intensely loyal to the Vesteys and most of them had spent their working lives with the company.

I personally felt very sorry when Jim Payne, Deputy Chairman of Blue Star Line and Edmund Vestey's brother-in-law, decided to "give up the rat-race" as he put it, in favour of setting up a salmon hatchery in the North West of Scotland. He was a thoroughly nice man with a sardonic sense of humour. At a reception following one of the Blue Star launches, he turned to me and said — "I'm very embarrassed at always being on the receiving end of the shipbuilders' hospitality. It's high time I reciprocated".

Thus it was arranged that he would call for my wife and me at the Smiths Dock flat in Whitehall Court, London and take us to dinner. We settled into the back of a Mercedes, whose driver proceeded across Westminster Bridge and took the first turning left on reaching the South Bank. We made our way slowly down a particularly seedy-looking street and stopped outside the most run-down building of all. We were led quickly through this uninhabited place and emerged at the rear of the building onto a gangway built out across the mud, leading to a barge sitting high and dry at low tide. Inside was beautifully decorated with a bar stretching along one side of the main compartment. After two enormous gin and tonics, we were invited to step outside and there, although we hadn't heard it arrive, stood a helicopter. My wife surprised me by asking Jim Payne whether she could take the seat next to the pilot. When she had been strapped in, the pilot handed her a road map which he would consult from time to time during the flight! Seconds later, we were whisked aloft, over St. Pauls Cathedral and the City of London and 20 minutes later we landed on the front lawn of the Payne residence in North Essex, ready for dinner. It beat launch receptions any day!

Like Alfred Holt, Blue Star Line involved itself in container ships. For this purpose it joined up with Cunard and Ellerman to form Associated Container Transportation (Australia) Ltd., — or A.C.T.A. for short. Between 1969 and 1977, seven large container ships were delivered to A.C.T.A. by Bremer Vulcan of Bremen. Bert Tune and his boys were technically responsible for the design and supervision of construction on behalf of the consortium.

Four reefers were delivered to Blue Star Line by Harland &

Wolff in the mid 80s. These fast and elegant vessels looked similar to the five built at Smiths Dock a decade earlier. Blue Star Line has now been in existence for exactly 80 years. I am confident that it will reach its Centenary.

CHAPTER 22

"BITS & PIECES"

A River Trip

CAPTAIN "Buck" Taylor was Lithgows "retained" pilot for most of the time I was fitting out ships for that company. Tall in stature, he was a striking figure in his navy blue uniform and peaked cap. He sported a pointed beard. The advantage of a retained pilot was that by paying a modest retainer, the shipyard could usually be assured of the services of an individual pilot, rather than one being allocated by the pilotage authority on a rota basis. By so doing, the yard believed that their chosen pilot could become loosely integrated into the management team and act at all times in the yard's best interests.

"Buck" had been a highly successful submarine captain during the War, but it soon became evident that, at the slightest provocation, he could become excitable and irritable. This may well have been the after-effects of his wartime exploits.

Six of the eight ships I outfitted were equipped with main machinery manufactured by David Rowan of Glasgow. Immediately after launch these vessels had to be towed 20 miles upriver and berthed at Stobcross Quay, under the big 150-ton hammerhead crane. The Clyde Navigation Trust's scale of charges for berthage was such that, provided the vessel was berthed for a period not exceeding 13 days, the charge per day was "X pounds". If for any reason, this period was exceeded, the charges per day were not increased for the excess period but for the whole period. Lithgows accordingly insisted that the machinery be installed within a 13-day period. Before installation could commence, the superstructure "loosework" had to be unshipped ashore by crane to expose the space through which the machinery could be lowered into the ship. Installation then began with the two sections of main engine bedplate, followed by two sections of crankcase and two of the entablature. Thereafter the smaller lifts of main engine exhausts and engine room overhauling crane were hoisted aboard. The shipyard then installed and connected the boiler flat, after which the boiler and uptakes were fitted. This complete, the shipyard then installed and fitted the casing top, after which the last lift — the funnel, was fitted. In order to meet the very tight deadline, it was frequently the case that our riveters were still riveting the casing top as the funnel was being lowered into place.

I never minded this period, since I was anxious to have the ship returned to the fitting-out basin in Port Glasgow as soon as possible and for one good reason. For the period the vessel was in Glasgow, our working hours remained unaltered i.e. a 7.30 a.m. start each morning which involved leaving home at an ungodly hour.

Lithgows also insisted that the vessel's return to Port Glasgow be undertaken at night, thus avoiding the loss of any working day. As on the tow upriver, the passage downriver was on the basis of a "dead ship". No power was available for winches on board. All ropes to tugs were manhandled by squads of shipyard labourers, as were the mooring ropes to the jetty.

At 2.00 a.m. on a cold winter's morning, the foreman shipwright, a handful of labourers and I sat huddled in a hut on deck awaiting the arrival of "Buck" Taylor and the tugs. The darkened superstructure of the vessel contained no completed accommodation. Most of it was bare steel with some piping, wiring and joiner work evident in the lower tiers. In due course, the tugs appeared out of the gloom, followed by "Buck". Then the gangway was removed, the tugs made fast forward and aft and the mooring lines cast off. Silently we set off downriver on our ghost-like trip, passing shipyards on either side, with the two tugs pulling us at a steady three or four knots.

The Upper Clyde has a number of bends and the one located just above John Brown's yard at Clydebank is the most acute. A huge warning notice to shipping reads — "Dead Slow". A wee boy on board a Clyde pleasure steamer asked his mother what the notice meant. She replied — "Hush son, do ye no ken, that's where your faither works!".

Beyond Clydebank, the river straightens and widens and at this point "Buck" relaxed and talked about life and in particular, how "hard done" he was. I had been to his house on a number of occasions, where he entertained royally. He loved working for Lithgows and I think he felt proud to have been selected as their "retained" pilot. He had one pet hate however in the shape of Jimmy Coburn, Lithgows Head Foreman Shipwright. I looked forward with keen anticipation to their next encounter which was very shortly due.

Dawn was about to break as we approached Lithgows outfitting basin. We began to make out a few huddled figures on the jetty. The figure of Jimmy Coburn stood alone like a hooded crow. The tugs began to ease the vessel through the 90° turn required to berth her, making due allowance for the wind and oncoming tide.

"Buck" began to get excited, giving frequent blasts of his whistle to the tugs. They were meant to acknowledge with blasts of their hooters — sometimes they didn't. Nine times out of ten, the ship hit the jetty with a sickening thud. At this point, the hooded crow suddenly came to life with what sounded suspiciously like shouted abuse at the pilot! "Buck", who wasn't especially pleased at what he believed was the tug's ineptitude, but furious that this incident had occurred under the nose of his enemy, gave vent to his emotions to anyone who would listen — "What's the old b - - - - - - shouting at?", he roared.

After a lot more whistle and hooter blasts, heaving and pulling, the ship was finally alongside. "Buck" relaxed, only to hear the now clear voice of Jimmy Coburn standing some distance up the jetty — "Move the ship another 100 feet up the jetty". On hearing this, "Buck" grabbed a megaphone, leaned over the bridge wing and roared — "Mr. Coburn, will you let me into your secret of how to berth a f - - - - - - ship at your jetty!".

"Buck" was still furious as we walked down the gangway some time later, with the ship safely moored. No sign of Jimmy Coburn — he had departed minutes before. There was "no welcome in the hillsides" from him on that or any other occasion.

The Cab Driver

In 1978, a colleague and I flew to Tampa on the Gulf Coast of Florida to try to drum up some reefer ship business. We had arranged to visit a Greek now resident in Saratoga and Uiterwyk, a Dutch reefer owner, located in Tampa.

We landed at Tampa airport on a beautiful sunny morning in

November and took a taxi to our hotel. Although only a short drive to the city centre, the driver impressed me, not only because of his pleasant manner but also because of his cultured conversation. It transpired that his name was George Paradise and that he had been made redundant as a school teacher in his native North Carolina.

Before arriving at the hotel, he politely enquired what our business was in Tampa. We told him and asked him the best way to reach Saratoga, some distance down the coast. He came into the hotel and over a cup of coffee, offered to drive us there himself. On hearing that he proposed a fixed charge which seemed eminently reasonable, we accepted.

He called for us at the time agreed and we set off down the coast on the very pleasant run to our destination, which turned out to be a holiday resort. With great difficulty, George finally located the address of the shipowner and as we got out of the cab, he shut the meter off.

We were shown into an elegant villa overlooking a creek in which were moored expensive looking launches. Pelicans perched on the branches of overhanging trees. A sound of muted classical music greeted our ears as the diminutive Greek doctor rose to greet us. He had sent me numerous telexed enquiries for updated prices of our reefer ships and I wanted to establish, once and for all, whether he had a genuine interest in placing a contract or was just testing the market. After an hour or so, I judged it was the latter and some little time later we took our leave.

There outside the villa stood our Yellow Cab with what was to become, for the next two days, our personal driver. George drove us back and en-route we stood him a drink. Further pleasant conversation on a variety of topics followed in the course of which he asked how long we proposed staying in Tampa. We told him that we had a meeting in Uiterwyk's offices timed for 10 a.m., following which we hoped to visit any other shipowners that might exist in the city. He proposed that we should use his cab for the whole of the next day and that, in the meantime, he would establish whether other shipowners operated out of Tampa.

The following day passed without any positive success businesswise but it felt great to have a car at one's disposal. Each time we left the cab the meter was switched off. The charges themselves were nominal. The reason George gave for offering his services was quite simple — he was bored driving people to and from the airport and he wanted someone to talk to. He apparently found us interesting — I think it might have been my Scottish accent!!

We gave him dinner that night and advised him that we were scheduled to leave the airport on the 4.00 p.m. flight to Mexico the following day. He then put forward a truly brilliant suggestion. Would we agree to his uplifting us from the hotel at 7.00 a.m. and driving us to Disney World at Orlando some 100 miles away? He told us that he was something of an expert guide since he had visited the place on nineteen occasions. He explained that Disney World covered a vast area and one could spend several days sampling its attractions and still not cover everything. He reckoned that we had five hours at our disposal on site and if we agreed to his suggestion, he would carefully select which delights to sample.

We of course accepted his proposal and precisely at 7.00 a.m. the next day set off for Orlando, passing many orange groves en-route. On arrival, he brought three sets of tickets for specific attractions explaining as we walked down "main street" that he was trying to give us as wide a selection as was possible in five hours. He did not tell us what each one was and I'm glad he didn't, for a reason that will shortly become clear.

We first entered a Ghost House with the sound of distant music in our ears. From an old gallery we looked down through windows hanging with cobwebs at couples in 19th Century evening clothes dancing a minuet — not real people of course.

We next climbed on to a slowly moving platform of seats, which on moving onwards revealed a harbour dominated by a sailing vessel firing its cannon over our heads. The thunder of the cannon and the explosions as the shells hit their targets were deafening. Some shots landed in the water close to the small boat on which we appeared to be sailing and huge columns of water rose high into the air. Figures were everywhere, firing cannon, falling off the rigging and overboard. We survived this onslaught and passed into a river mouth with the noise fading behind us. A peaceful scene met our eyes as we made our way upriver past beaches crawling with crabs and backed by cottages with their owners asleep in the sun while dogs were scampering around the gardens. Again, it was so lifelike that it was hard to believe it was unreal.

We made visits to other attractions but suddenly I saw it — a great pyramid of a building with at its entrance a notice which warned — "People suffering from any kind of giddiness or any kind of heart complaint should not enter this building". The penny didn't drop until we were inside awaiting the arrival of the roller-coaster. We climbed on board and were securely strapped in by attendants. I noticed that handgrips were provided! I was petrified! The train began to move slowly through an opening and we were on our way uphill through a tunnel of flame, only there was no heat. On disappearing through an opening at the top of the tunnel, it was pitch black as we were suddenly accelerated over a huge hump into the empty blackness below. My eyes became accustomed to the darkness but I quickly shut them! My stomach was everywhere but the right place. At last we slowed down and emerged into the daylight. As I released myself from my seat I felt 100 years old! But as I began to walk away I felt ten feet tall. George told us — "This is the fastest roller-coaster in the U.S.A.". I didn't doubt it.

He drove us back to Tampa and we boarded our flight for Mexico. I was sorry to leave Florida.

S-Bends

As a ship approaches its launch on a date set usually set some time ago, the pace of work noticeably increases as everyone concerned tries to meet the deadline. A tendency to "cut corners" can creep in during such a phase. A succession of 14,000 ton deadweight ore carriers built by Lithgows were equipped with a dry cargo tank between No. 1 hold and the Fore Peak tank. As the launch date drew near, the outstanding steel work still to be completed became more and more confined to the fore end of the vessel, namely the dry cargo tank and the Fore Peak tank. The *Ripon*, one of the ore carriers in question and built for the North Yorkshire Shipping Company, was duly delivered and entered service. After 12 months in service, the ship was stemmed for drydocking in South Wales — the "guarantee drydock".

Since I had been the manager in charge of outfitting the ship, it fell to me to visit the vessel in South Wales and hopefully come to an agreement with the owners as to the shipbuilder's liabilities under guarantee. I arrived at the shiprepairer's yard and decided to have a cursory look at the vessel before presenting myself to the owners. I was appalled by what I saw! A shell plate had been removed from the port side of the vessel's dry cargo tank. A gangway led from the dockside through the opening thus made onto scaffolding inside the tank. Boilermakers were burning out rivets connecting the main framing to the shell plating. I picked up one of the rivets that had just been released — there was nothing wrong with it! Although still warm, I placed it in my coat pocket and climbed back to the dockside. Along the edge of the dock were lying rivets evidently burned out from the ship. They were indeed in bad shape — like a figure 'S'. It was clear that the holes into which they had been originally driven had been well out of line. I carefully kicked them all into the dock and then proceeded on board.

The chief superintendent was an experienced and friendly man in his fifties. I was young and inexperienced, but determined to defend my employer. He sat in the captain's cabin and on the table in front of him, stood a Gold Flake tobacco tin. After welcoming me, he explained that he was not at all happy with some aspects of the yard's riveting. As evidence of his contention, he opened the tin and revealed four rivets that looked very bent indeed and asked me what I had to say about this?

I immediately asked where he had come by these, since I had noticed rivets of a similar deformity lying on the bottom of the dock and which could have come from an infinite number of previous ship repairs. I produced a still slightly warm rivet from my pocket and told him that, in my presence, this perfectly good rivet had been burned out from the vessel for no apparent reason. Accordingly therefore my company could not be held liable for the cost of replacement.

He had listended to me with considerable tolerance and finally said with a smile — "You've got a bloody nerve" and closed the tobacco tin. We then managed to negotiate a reasonable settlement.

Rivets, whose rivets?

A Little Light Music

I am fond of listening to dance music and traditional jazz played on the piano. I encountered on my travels piano players in hotel bars in the United States, Canada, India and elsewhere. I usually asked them to play one of my favourites — "Fly Me to the Moon" and then silently awarded them marks out of ten! I also like South

American rhythms, especially the Bosanova. I imagine this is difficult to play.

One night in Bombay, our shiprepair agent announced that he would take a colleague and me to a nightclub, which formed part of a big hotel. When we got there, our agent was mortified to discover that since it was a Sunday evening, there was no floorshow. Entertainment was limited to a 16-piece dance orchestra and because of this, apart from one other table, the place was deserted. The members of the orchestra looked pretty glum during their frequent pauses between playing. I asked them whether they could play the Bosanova. What followed was, at least to my ears, one of the best musical evenings of my life. They played at least six Bosanovas, hardly without a pause, in the most melodious and rhythmical manner, with frequent solo contributions. They and we thoroughly enjoyed ourselves.

In Japan I encountered "Karaoke", that is to say, music played in a novel way. Many of the tiny bars dotted about the centre of Shimonoseki were equipped with high-quality stereo equipment fitted with head-phones. After a few drinks, our Japanese hosts suggested I might like to sing. There was no excuse for saying — "I don't know the words", as I was pressed to thumb through a huge volume of well-known songs, with words written in both Japanese and English. Having selected a song, you were then handed a microphone and the headphones placed in position. The result of all this was, judging by the giggling Japanese, hilarious. Here was I, singing "Fly Me to the Moon" backed by a truly first-class dance orchestra. This unlikely blend of great music and gravelly voice was being broadcast across the crowded little bar! So far as I was concerned, this rendering of my favourite tune rated the lowest marks of all!

Windrose

One of the most unusual projects to come my way occurred in 1980. When Smiths Dock first received the enquiry for a square-rigged barque. I was inclined to place the relevant documents in the waste-paper basket and it wasn't until I met the driving force behind this project that I was persuaded to consider it seriously. I couldn't fail but be carried along by the enthusiasm and dedication of the driving force in question — Captain Mike

Willoughby by name. A master mariner, he had in fact sailed square-riggers across the oceans of the world.

He had conceived the idea of constructing a 10,000 ton deadweight sailing ship, equipped with modestly-powered main machinery, capable of transporting general cargo over long distances for a fraction of the cost of conventional tonnage.

In particular, he was aiming at regular round voyages between the U.K. and Australia. He explained, with the aid of numerous charts, that he considered that for only a very few days of the passage, both outward and homeward bound, would main engines be the sole means of driving the vessel forward. This occurred in the area known as The Doldrums. Elsewhere, the vessel required either no assistance from the main machinery because of the prevailing winds or some assistance in other areas. On this basis he had calculated the mean average speed and the total fuel consumption.

Warming to his theme, he went on to explain the crew numbers involved and their cost per voyage. He outlined the features of the vessel, which among other things was to be equipped with electric sliding steel hatch covers together with a number of electric winches for raising and lowering the sails. In order to boost revenue, he proposed that the ship accommodate 50 passengers. He was convinced that there were enough adventurous people who would be prepared to pay good money for the experience of a long sea voyage in a sailing ship.

The company that would own the vessel was called Windrose Shipping and it had commissioned a prominent U.K. consultant Naval Architect to design the vessel, within the basic parameters laid down by Captain Willoughby. What was now urgently required was an estimate of construction cost and hopefully a subsidised one!

At this point I was concerned for a number of reasons. First, although relieved that the design was not our responsibility, I had to ensure that contractually we would not be held liable for any shortfall in the ship's performance — viz. speed, stability, deadweight etc. Second, I was not willing for our company being held responsible for the manufacture and erection of the masts, spars, sails and rigging. Third, was this a commercial proposition that would attract finance? I was to be satisfied on all three counts. It was agreed that the contract would contain no penalty clauses, other than for delivery. Insofar as masts etc. were concerned, this work would be undertaken by a specialist and the various items installed at his premises after we had completed all hull and machinery work. The financial justification was the most telling point.

Windrose had in mind trying to persuade the Australian Wool Board to enter into a 15 year charter for the carriage of wool to the U.K. Windrose believed that the cost per deadweight ton would prove highly attractive and that armed with a 15 year charter there would be no difficulties in raising the finance from U.K. banks.

We agreed to work up an estimate of cost and apply for Intervention Fund Subsidy. Shortly afterwards we received various plans and design calculations from the subject Naval Architect and in due course submitted our price. It benefited from a subsidy. This price was accepted and used to calculate the rate for carrying Australian wool.

No sooner had our price been submitted than it was announced that all concerned were to meet the members of the Australian Wool Board who had a number of meetings scheduled in Pall Mall offices in London. It was proposed that each party to the project would give a presentation to the Board — Captain Willoughby on the overall project, the Naval Architect on the design, me on the construction and the Banks on finance.

We duly met the Board and gave our presentations. We were listened to attentively and a great many questions were asked and there seemed to be a real note of optimism in the air. Clearly the Board were impressed. They undertook to give us their decision within a matter of weeks. They apparently had no choice since the current wool charter was nearing expiry.

We were all very sad to learn shortly afterwards that the offer had not been accepted. I suspected that a number of powerful lobbies had been at work in both political and shipping circles to persuade the Wool Board to stick to conventional shipping. Without the wool charter, the project was not viable.

I don't think that I had the wool pulled over my eyes! Ewe can't win them all!

The Big City

I made my first business trip to the City of London shortly after joining Smiths Dock in May 1973. I had no conception about how to sell ships nor did I have many contacts with owners' superintendents

other than those I came across when working for Swan Hunter. I
didn't think it a good idea to "touch base" with them in case it be
thought that I was trying to bite the hand that fed me!

I started with Furness Withy in Fenchurch Street and there I was
courteously received by a member of their senior staff that I had
known for some years. He was at once prepared to give me his
views on the current state of the shipping market. I next called on
Blue Star Line at their offices in West Smithfield. We already had
three orders from them and so there was much to discuss.

It wasn't too long before I felt comfortable about arranging an
appointment with shipowners and thereafter discussing the
possibility of newbuildings. Gradually I widened the circle of
shipowning acquaintances and over the years that followed hugely
enjoyed my visits to their offices. Shipowners like anyone else come
in different shapes and sizes and while they were almost always
friendly, the two shipowners' staffs that I felt most at home with
were Blue Star Line and Manchester Liners.

Blue Star's offices were sparse and so far as the technical
department was concerned — cramped. There I met Bert Tune and
his technical staff. They were a small efficient team and very
friendly. Over the next few years, Smiths Dock built ten ships for
Blue Star and their associates. It was a happy and fruitful
relationship.

Following a successful negotiation with say a foreign shipowner,
contract signing formalised the proceedings. Here one met Bankers,
officials from the Export Credit Guarantee Department and
Lawyers. They were each concerned with the considerable
paperwork involved — the ship contract between owner and
builder, the loan agreement between the Bank and Owner and the
specific guarantee from E.C.G.D.

Some bankers I found somewhat pompous. They all had one
thing in common though. They didn't just want their bread buttered
on both sides — they wanted jam on both sides as well! Compared
to the risks being taken by the Shipbuilder, the Shipowner and
E.C.G.D., the Banker's risks were minimal. But their insistence on
security against the loan was total. The Shipbuilder had quoted a
fixed price for the manufacture of a highly complex product not
due for delivery for some considerable time in the future. Many
things can occur to inflate the Shipbuilder's costs and in such cases

the Shipbuilder picks up the tab. The Shipowner cannot guarantee that his market will remain stable for the 20 year life of the ship or even indeed for the 7 year loan repayment period. His risks are considerable. E.C.G.D. guaranteed the repayment of the bank loan by the Shipowner. In the event that the Shipowner went into liquidation, E.C.G.D. had to repay all but 10% of the balance of the original loan to the bank. There have been numerous cases of this in recent years and so E.C.G.D. was very much involved in the risk business.

E.C.G.D.'s offices were terribly drab affairs equipped with cheap furniture and small carpet runners. I always felt sorry for their officials, but over the years came to appreciate just what risks they were prepared to take. I don't mean to imply that they were in any way rash but rather that they tried to help the builder gain the business, even although some of the shipowners concerned were from foreign countries whose economies were decidedly fragile.

Manchester Liners' offices were located in Manchester, not far from the docks. Their staff occupied a number of floors of a modern bow-fronted office block. The directors and senior staff were all housed on the top floor with panoramic views of Greater Manchester — if you like that sort of thing! The Board were great leg-pullers and lunches were normally hilarious events. We did a lot of business here.

The majority of U.K. shipping business was conducted in the City of London but not just by shipowners but also by shipbrokers. A great number of them were located there. They too I found easy to get on with. They are the pulse of the shipping market and from them one could sometimes learn of specific owners' future intentions. It was important to "show the flag" to brokers so that in the event of an enquiry for a ship, one's company was on the broker's list.

Some shipbuilders held strongly to the view that shipbrokers were an unnecessary evil and that the 1% commission that they charged the builder for introducing the business was largely unearned. Certainly some brokers confined their activity to sending out enquiries. The yard that eventually won the business was of course charged the brokerage fee. In such cases, the brokerage has not been earned in my opinion. Other brokers however maintained contact with the subject yard, feeding it with information concerning the competition as well as the owner's reactions to the various quotations. Such brokers most certainly earned their commission.

Shipbrokers seemed to revel in chaos insofar as paperwork is concerned. On meeting a broker, I was normally shown into a small conference room, given a cup of coffee and thereafter discussions took place in a civilised fashion. But open the conference room door and there it was — one large office, brokers shouting into telephones, telex machines chattering, telexes heaped on telexes, paper on the floor — a shambles! But it worked! I once defined a shipbroker with tongue-in-cheek as — "Someone who talks himself into sending a shipbuilder a bill, with a letter introducing himself!"

I remember once having some problems with a U.K. Shipowner. His Scottish Banker rang me one morning in my office in Middlesbrough. In precise Edinburgh tones he began — "Good morning Mr. Parker. It's a lovely day here, but wait a moment — I see a big dark cloud and it's heading your way!"

So far as contracts are concerned, I coined two definitions. "Force Majeure" — that's French for — "I told you it would happen". "Delivery Date" — "That's when second-class letters arrive!".

CHAPTER 23

POSTSCRIPT

THE decline of the U.K. Shipbuilding industry which began in the early 50s, gathered momentum due to a combination of circumstances. I have already referred to the lead that Sweden had taken in shipbuilding technology following the end of the Second World War; and to the emergence of the Japanese shipbuilding industry; and to the reconstruction of West German shipyards. I also referred to the fact that in this period when U.K. shipbuilders had invested in new plant and equipment, productivity had begun to fall.

In the late 50s and early 60s, many countries set up their own shipbuilding industries and in a remarkably short space of time, became proficient in the business and with the benefit of cheap labour, not to mention Government assistance. Of these, Brazil and particularly South Korea, became a serious threat to the future of the U.K. Shipbuilding Industry. By the 70s, world shipbuilding capacity had massively increased with the Chinese coming on stream.

The shipping market meanwhile had exhibited its usual ups and downs from 1950 to the early 70s, but by 1975 was firmly depressed and was to remain that way until 1990. The net result was huge overcapacity in World shipbuilding leading to price cutting and to subsidies, as Governments struggled to avoid large-scale unemployment. Thus, by the time the decision was taken in 1976 by the Callaghan Government to Nationalise the Shipbuilding Industry, the competition had never been so great, nor our ability to compete, so fragile.

Had no action been taken at this time, many yards of course would have gone out of business, as had happened in previous periods of depression. But why Nationalise in order to try to preserve the industry? The West Germans didn't and a fair proportion of their shipbuilding capability remains intact today. The reason of course was political. It formed part of the Labour Party's programme and the shipbuilding unions welcomed the prospect. British Shipbuilders lasted in all but name for little more than 10 years and throughout that period, staggered from one financial crisis to the next, amid sell-offs, contraction and redundancies, until it was left in 1987 with some 6,000 people, before finally being wound up shortly thereafter.

The commercial facts of life were primarily responsible for this unhappy end. The Intervention Fund Subsidy which over the years peaked at 30%, but which on average was pitched at some 25% of the U.K. break-even price, was intended to enable us to match Far East competition. It never did, for two reasons. First, the South Koreans were quoting prices equivalent to the material cost in our tenders i.e. 65% of price. The subsidy could not bridge this gap. Second, although our low productivity was one cause of an unnecessarily high price, the resulting labour cost totalled only some 15% of that price. A huge increase in productivity would have been required to finally close the gap. This was not forthcoming. The result was that losses were being recorded on many contracts, although the subsidy was payable in theory only if the contract broke even.

Most of the Corporate Plans presented each year to Government recorded large contract losses, large unrecovered overheads and high capital expenditure for the year past. The plans budgeted for four years hence — modest contract losses but usually large unrecovered overheads and capital expenditure. In the year following, the results were usually very different with the contract losses greatly exceeding budget. There is no way that an industry in private hands could have afforded the losses or the level of unrecovered overheads. And in the circumstances in which they found themselves, I suspect that a private company would have placed an embargo on capital expenditure.

Government's decision to privatise the naval yards was of course the beginning of the end for the Corporation, because the profits generated by the Naval Builders could not then be offset against the larger losses generated by the rest of the Corporation's activities.

Corporation Board member appointments were made in the name of the Secretary of State for Trade and Industry, but the method of selection remains a mystery to me. The appointments were for a tenure of three years. Now a week may be a long time in politics but three years is not very long in shipbuilding. After all, it didn't even span the period of one Corporate Plan. Moreover, it takes longer than three years to deliver one Naval ship from date of contract. There could be no continuity with such a system. Few of those so appointed had their contract extended. So it appears that neither Government not the appointee expected more than a three year stint in shipbuilding. What kind of commitment is this? This was in stark contrast to people like me who had laboriously worked their way up through the ranks and provided both continuity and commitment to our chosen profession.

Of course there were other factors which caused the demise of much of the Industry. One of these was labour. For almost 30 years, I had to deal with industrial relations and certainly I had more than my fair share of strikes, go-slows, overtime bans and the like. That said, I don't believe it was very good anywhere across the Industry. While incidents of this kind were directly responsible for delayed deliveries, contract losses, loss of reputation and rightly received a good deal of adverse Press comment, the lack of productivity was much more serious. Put another way — had the same level of strikes etc. prevailed but been accompanied by an acceptable productivity level, then the Industry might well have survived in larger measure. Over many years both before and after Nationalis-ation, much thought was given to this problem. However well one might succeed in eliminating demarcation, introducing better working practices and increasing levels of automation, four hours work for eight hours pay is a disaster in anyone's language.

Management must accept its share of the blame for this consistent failure to improve the use of the working day. This blame attaches as much to management prior to Nationalisation as after it. But one feature of management has to be borne in mind. The inexorable decline of the industry over several decades had attracted comparatively few bright young men into its fold. Those few who were attracted, tended to gravitate into the technical area.

In more recent times some were attracted into Computer Technology. Not surprisingly, few if any wanted anything to do with Production or Labour Relations. Production of course is where "the buck stops". There is no doubt that a dearth of good production managers had become more and more evident. The net result in most yards was that more and more reliance was placed in a diminishing number of production managers. So, where it mattered most — "AT THE SHARP END" — management was growing ever weaker.

Of all the factors which caused the demise of the bulk of Merchant Shipbuilding in the U.K., by far the most crucial was the commercial factor. Had we not been Nationalised but had still been in receipt of government subsidy, as in West Germany, there might have been more left of the Industry today. But that alas is pure speculation.

I and I suspect many others, mourn the loss of most of a great Industry.